The Man They Wouldn't Let Die

ALEXANDER DOROZYNSKI

The Man
They Wouldn't
Let Die

THE MACMILLAN COMPANY, *New York*

Acknowledgment is gratefully made to the following copyright holders for permission to reprint from previously published materials:

Simon and Schuster, Inc. and J. Robert Oppenheimer for permission to use an excerpt from *Science and the Common Understanding* by J. Robert Oppenheimer, a series of Reith lectures given on the BBC in London in 1953. Copyright 1953, 1954 by J. Robert Oppenheimer.

Nature magazine for permission to use an excerpt from an article by Professor Leon Rosenfeld which appeared in Number 190 of that magazine. Copyright 1961, *Nature* magazine, London.

Pergamon Press, Inc. for permission to use an excerpt from the chapter by Professor Leon Rosenfeld, "On Quantum Electrodynamics," in *Niels Bohr and the Development of Physics*. Copyright 1955 by Pergamon Press, Inc.

The New York Times for permission to use an excerpt from "Soviet Atom Lead Overcome by U.S." by Harry Schwartz. Copyright 1954 by the New York Times Company. Reprinted by permission.

Pergamon Press, Inc. for permission to use an excerpt from *The Restoration of Function After Brain Injury* by Alexander Luriia. Copyright 1963 by Pergamon Press, Inc.

The Bollingen Foundation and Routledge and Kegan Paul, Ltd., London, for permission to use an excerpt from the Vladimir Nabokov translation of *Eugene Onegin* by Alexander Pushkin. Copyright 1964 by the Bollingen Foundation, New York. Reprinted by permission.

First Printing

The Macmillan Company, New York
Collier-Macmillan Canada, Ltd., Toronto, Ontario

Library of Congress catalog card number: 65-15181

Printed in the United States of America

TO ARIANE

ACKNOWLEDGMENTS

The cooperation of many was needed to overcome the difficulties of gathering material for this story. I would like to thank in particular Professor Nikolai Grashchenkov, Mrs. Concordia Landau, Professor Alexei Abrikossov, Professor Alim Damir, Professor Yevgheni Lifshitz, and Danil Danin (the author of a fascinating book about physics, *The Inescapable Strange World*), in the Soviet Union; Professor and Mrs. George Gamow of Boulder, Colorado; Professor Leon Rosenfeld of Copenhagen; Professor and Mrs. Rudolph Peierls of Oxford; Professor Wilder Penfield of Montreal; Robert Maxwell of Oxford; Eugene Kone, Dr. John Prutting, Fred Jaffe and William H. White of New York; Robert Markel of The Macmillan Company; and also Mrs. Barbara Land, for her valuable professional advice; General Guillain de Benouville of Paris, for a *coup de piston* at the right time; and Mrs. Lewis G. Morris, whose confidence was particularly helpful in moments of discouragement.

CONTENTS

When I traveled to Moscow in Summer, 1962, the name
of Lev Landau was only vaguely familiar to me. As a rule,
the Soviet Press does not publish reports about traffic
accidents, and there had been no mention that Landau
had nearly died in one. It was only by chance that I met,
shortly before my departure, one of Landau's acquaint-
ances, who told me of Landau's achievements as a scientist,
of his strength and originality as a person, and who told
me also of a small new world that had taken shape within
the Soviet metropolis, a world dedicated to saving the life
of a man who was still unconscious and should have been
dead.

Such was his enthusiasm in speaking about Landau and
about the dozens of people who were striving to help him
recover, and the story he hinted at seemed so unusual,
that I decided to take the opportunity of another trip to
Moscow, to find out more about it and to meet Landau
himself, if he were still alive.

The task seemed to be simple enough, until I ran head-
long into Soviet bureaucracy. Bureaucracies can be painful
to deal with anywhere in the world, but particularly so
when you are a Western journalist who travels to a Communist country with the specific and suspicious purpose
of finding out about a Soviet physicist. One trip to
Moscow was almost entirely wasted in dealing with that
bureaucracy, which was a necessary step (I had been told)

to reach anyone whose words might be quoted in the West.

On a second trip to gather information about what had become known as "The Miracle of Moscow," I attempted as much as possible to bypass official channels, with some success. Once personal contacts had been established, I found in many of Landau's friends unusual warmth and frankness, and the possibility of a relationship on a level I had not been led to expect.

I am thankful for the cooperation of Landau's friends in the Soviet Union and abroad, whose admiration for him was so apparent. And to Landau himself, in whom I found the kindness and the desire to please which I had been led to expect.

I am thankful also to the Novosti Press Agency, and particularly to Irina Anatolievna Lunacharskaya, a most charming science reporter, for assistance in gathering some of the material for this story.

At the same time, I extend my apologies to Professor Landau and to his friends for the errors which, inevitably, they will find in this book. In the hectic days that followed the accident, many people contributed more than could have been expected of anybody, and the team that spontaneously formed around Landau is a rare example of humanity at its best. But it did not distinguish itself for keeping records. So many conflicting stories have since circulated about "The Miracle of Moscow" that it was difficult to weed out fancy from fact. Some of the events of Landau's past life, also, may not be entirely accurate, as many have to do with matters about which no records are kept, or if kept, are not readily made available. The story, nevertheless, seems worth telling.

This book is not intended as a political polemic, and if

references are made to certain aspects of Marxism-Leninism, it is because they turned out to be important to the story. I should point out, perhaps, that criticisms of the system come neither from Landau nor from the people I have met in Moscow, but from myself. I can only hope that they are objective, though it may be presumptuous to hope that they may also be constructive.

The Man They Wouldn't Let Die

CHAPTER 1

Avaria
on Dimitrovsky Highway

ON JANUARY 7, 1962, Moscow awakened under a thin sheet of ice. The night had been rainy and unseasonably warm. The chill returned in the morning, instantly freezing the water to the roads, houses, and trees. Then, the ice was covered with a thin layer of dry, crisp snow flakes.

Driving was dangerous and exasperatingly slow. It was Sunday and the usually efficient street-cleaning teams and their rumbling snow-removal machinery were a bit late with their work when the telephone rang in the garage of the academy of Sciences on Leninsky Prospect.

"Landau calling," said the voice. "I need a car right away for Dubna."

The dispatcher was not surprised. Sunday or not, you never could tell why nor when a physicist would decide to head for Dubna, the Soviet "city of the atom" north of Moscow. Professor Lev Davidovich Landau, as a full member of the Academy of Sciences, was entitled to a car with chauffeur any time he wanted one, but today the dispatcher had been warned about the dangerous condition of the roads.

"I am sorry, Lev Davidovich. I can't give you a car today. Roads are murderous."

"But I have to go to Dubna," said Landau. He didn't mention that he wasn't going there to work, but to visit relatives who were having matrimonial problems he wanted to look into.

"Sorry, we have no cars today."

Landau knew better than to insist. He had no car and did not drive; his reflexes were so slow that he had consistently failed to pass his driver's test. He decided to call one of his friends, physicist Vladimir Sudakov, who agreed to drive him to Dubna.

Half an hour later Sudakov's car drove up to Landau's small duplex apartment on the grounds of the Institute of Physical Problems on Vorobiovskya Chaussée in the southern section of the city. Landau seated himself in the back seat, on the right of Sudakov's wife Vera, who moved out of his way a basket of eggs she was taking to their friends in Dubna. Slowly, the car took the road northward, crossing the Moskva River, passing the Kremlin walls, and following fashionable Gorki Street. The heater purred comfortably and Landau removed his fur hat and coat, revealing a gaunt, tall figure, topped by an abundant mane of wavy dark hair streaked with white. He sprawled awkwardly on the seat, talking with animation.

The Volga sedan, the most common Soviet passenger car, was now rolling through the vast and lackluster northern suburbs of Moscow along Dimitrovsky Highway. Vera was still bundled up in her thick *shuba*, and Vladimir Sudakov was intent upon the ice-covered road.

Suddenly a small girl ran across the street toward a bus

that was stopped ahead. Sudakov jammed on the brakes and the Volga started skidding out of control, spinning slowly, finally to stop, unharmed, on the left side of the road. The right side of the car, where Landau was sitting, faced a truck coming from the opposite direction.

The truck wasn't going rapidly and its driver expertly started pumping on the brakes to avoid hitting the Volga. But the road was too slick. With slow deliberation the truck skidded on, striking the car. The impact was not particularly violent but in the back seat, Landau's bony frame was caught and squeezed between the right door and the bundled-up Vera Sudakova, who was thrown against him. Landau's slow reflexes had not warned him in time, and he took the blow completely relaxed, his head whipping sideways like that of a disarticulated puppet. "It must have been like shaking Don Quixote in a tin can," one of his friends later commented. "But a Don Quixote whose bones had remained chalky and fragile ever since he was released from jail more than twenty years earlier."

Stunned, Sudakov stepped out on the pavement. The truck driver, a husky man with a black leather hat and fur flaps covering his ears, jumped out, took in the scene, went to the Volga's rear door and opened it. Landau's body slumped out, apparently lifeless, his chest pushed in, his long legs strangely angled to his body, his forehead cracked open, blood oozing out of his ears. They stretched him on the icy road, covering him with blankets and overcoats. The truck driver ran and found a telephone booth, from which first aid can be called without using a coin. He dialed the number - - 3 - - and reported the accident: "*Avaria** on Dimitrovsky Chaussée. One man seems to be dead, but I'm not sure. Send an ambulance, quickly."

---

* *Avaria*, a word originally meaning "damage" or "mishap", has come to be used currently in reference to traffic accidents.

Neither Sudakov nor his wife was injured. On the back seat of the Volga, the eggs weren't even broken.

Minutes later a first-aid ambulance drove Landau and the Sudakovs to the nearest hospital, Hospital No. 50 of Moscow's Timiriasevsky District. The physician on duty examined the patient stretched out on the operating table in the emergency room, shrugged his shoulders, listened to his heart. "He's still alive," he said, almost as if surprised.

"It's Landau," said one of the stretcher-bearers.

"The physicist? Call Yegorova," said the young doctor. With the assistance of a nurse, he started cutting away the scientist's blood-stained clothes.

The hospital's chief physician was out of town and his assistant, Dr. Nina Yegorova, wearing a housecoat, was going about domestic chores in her apartment across the street when the telephone rang, announcing that Academician Lev Davidovich Landau, the Soviet Union's top nuclear physicist and theoretician, had been brought, dying, to the hospital.

Throwing a thick *shuba* over her house-dress, she ran across the street from her home to the hospital. A first examination revealed a list of injuries that seemed to leave no hope for survival:

Fracture of nine ribs, some of which had pierced the airtight membrane containing the lungs. On the left side, there was a pneumothorax, the total collapse of the lung, filling the pleural cavity with air. On the right, a hemothorax: the membrane containing the lung was filled with blood, and the lung was partly collapsed.

Rupture of the symphisis pubis, the articulation between the pubic bones. All of the three pubic bones themselves—the pubis, ischium, and ilium, seemed to be broken, as well as the femur of the left leg.

The shattered pubic bones had torn through organs of the abdominal cavity, but the damage could not yet be estimated.

Landau was completely unconscious. Breathing was faint and irregular—only superficial breathing, because only part of one lung still functioned, and probably also because of the irritation that the broken ribs would cause during deep inhalation. Heart-beat was also irregular. Damage of the brain centers controlling the "automatic" functions of the body was suspected.

The scientist was dying.

On that chilly Sunday afternoon, there was no mention of the accident in the newspapers or on the radio, but the news rapidly spread through Moscow.

CHAPTER 2

The Promises
of Youth

(1908–1929)

LEV LANDAU was born on January 22, 1908, in Baku, on the west coast of the Caspian Sea. Before it became the center of Russia's petroleum wealth at the beginning of the century, Baku was a quiet Muslim city of white, flat-roofed houses and narrow streets winding down from Khan Sarai, the palace and fortress of its fifteenth-century ruler. Glistening under the subtropical sun, the old town was dotted with mosques, minarets, noisy Oriental markets, and tiny sidewalk cafés. An industrial district was rapidly growing around the harbor, soon to be covered with soot and dust, earning the name of "black town."

A year before Landau's birth one Joseph Dzhugashvili, a former student in a theological seminary, had come to Baku where he engaged in revolutionary activities, fanning unrest and organizing strikes. Stalin's brief passage

through the oil city left behind the beginnings of a Bolshevik organization, ready to act on orders from above.

Not far from the "black town" was the residential district of Baku, known as "the white town," where lived
Lev's father David, a petroleum engineer, and his mother,
a physician. Little Lev was an exceptionally bright boy; at
four, he could read; at five, he was a shy, awkward, and
bony schoolboy, who didn't particularly like to play with
his classmates and avoided fighting with them. They were
much bigger and older and stronger than he, and he preferred to read or to play with the numbers and geometric
figures that came dancing into his head. Now and then his
father would help him solve a problem, but it was pretty
much on his own that, by age of seven, Lev completed his
own course in high school math.

The boy liked to listen to and take part in grownups'
conversations. He frowned attentively when his parents
talked of unrest in Czarist Russia, trying to understand not
only what was happening, but why. When the Revolution
broke out, ten-year old Lev Landau could participate in
serious discussions about its aims and probable outcome.
Many of the leading revolutionaries were Jews, and he
felt that the new order would bring, no doubt, a new
freedom to the long-oppressed Jewish minorities in Russia. "Who knows," Papa David would say, tousling his
child's unruly, curly hair, "perhaps our Levka will be
going to the university one day!" David himself had been
one of the fortunate few to have been admitted under the
Jewish quota to a Russian university under the Czars.

In 1918, when Lev was a student at the gymnasium
(approximately the equivalent of an American high
school) Baku fell to the Bolsheviks. Weeks later it was
recaptured by the Whites, then taken over by a local

movement, the Moussavatists, who attempted to secede from the newborn Soviet Union, proclaiming Azerbaidzhan an independent state. On April 28, 1920, Baku fell again to the Red Armies, to become the capital of the Azerbaidzhan Soviet Socialist Republic.

Finishing high school at thirteen, Lev Landau hoped to sign up at the mathematics faculty in the University of Baku, but his father had planned for him a more practical, administrative or financial career. Heartbroken, Lev dragged his feet to the Economics Technicum, studied there for a year, then, in utter frustration, refused to go on. There was no choice but to let him into the university, where he became the youngest student, majoring both in mathematics and in physics.

He graduated two years later, thirsting for more knowledge. His teachers at the University of Baku had enthusiastically recommended him to the faculty of the University of Petrograd and to the institutes where Yoffe, Frenkel, Fok, the most famed Russian physicists, were beginning to teach the still rudimentary concepts of the emerging quantum physics.

After Lenin's death in January 1924, Petrograd, having once been St. Petersburg, became Leningrad. A few months later Lev Landau, a tall, skinny youth of sixteen, endowed with a magnificent set of buck teeth, an unruly flock of wavy dark hair, with a dream in his eyes, was given a railroad ticket, pocket money, and a letter to his aunt in Leningrad. Loaded with books, warm clothes, and a heavy food basket, he boarded the train at Baku in the summer of 1924, for the long journey to Leningrad and to fame.

When Peter the Great founded St. Petersburg in 1703, he considered this new window to the Baltic and to the

Western World so important to the future of Russia that he forbade any other stone construction to be undertaken in the Russian Empire, lest the new metropolis suffer from a shortage of stone cutters. The monumental, eccentric city was shaped by the Italian architect Bartolomeo Rastrelli, and even after the Soviet Revolution, the beauty of the Northern Venice in the midst of the Neva and its canals, ignoring the pockmarks of bullets, seemed to wait for the return of the Czar's Cossacks to restore a preposterously disturbed order of things. The magnificent monuments resisted the invasion of the gray, uniform buildings that were giving the Soviet Union its blank new face. Rastrelli's pale-green Winter Palace, Falconet's equestrian statue of Peter the Great, Quarenghi's Hermitage and State Bank, the pink column of Alexander, the canary-yellow Admiralty with its shining spire, the brick-colored fortress of Peter and Paul where Dostoesky faced a mock firing squad, presented a colorful, strangely anachronistic background to the throngs of drably dressed comrades who paraded along the city's wide avenues at the slightest excuse.

When Landau reached Leningrad, a political struggle for power was shaping the future of the Soviet Union, the future also of Soviet science. Many historians agree that when Lenin, half-paralyzed and almost totally incapacitated, died, whatever had existed of revolutionary integrity was trampled down and died out. Lenin's intellectual peer and heir apparent was Lev Davidovich Bronstein, alias Trotsky, a brilliant orator, former president of the Petrograd Soviet, organizer and commander-in-chief of the Red Army. But Trotsky was kept from power by a triumvirate that held the new nation in an iron fist: Stalin, Kamenev, and Zinoviev (earlier known or, rather, un-

known, as Dzhugashvili, Rosenfeld, and Apfelbaum).
After the trio's rise to power Stalin slowly but surely
forged ahead, supported by a group of Old Bolsheviks.
Stalin's chief weapon was terror, wielded by Yagoda, chief
of the dreaded secret police, the OGPU. Trotsky could
not hold out against Stalin. In 1929 he was expelled from
the party, and driven out of Russia. Stalin was now dictator absolute. Newspapers proclaimed the ideological,
agricultural, and industrial achievements of the new state,
but the people lived in poverty, in fear of imminent arrest,
brainwashed with patriotic and revolutionary slogans.

Yet, when Landau came to Leningrad, he found an
atmosphere surprisingly favorable to an eager young
student. From its beginning, the new order had supported
science and helped scientists—Marxism itself being considered as a science, rather than an ideology. Science was
viewed as a tool to discover more about the universe, to
feed the masses, to discredit religion, and generally to
further communism, whereas in Czarist times, few scientific researchers received government support, and those
who accomplished anything did it pretty much on their
own, with the support of wealthy patrons, or abroad. It is
significant enough that even as the Revolution went on,
between 1918 and 1920, one hundred and seventeen scientific institutions were created on Lenin's directives.

Meanwhile, relativity and quantum mechanics were
born and coming of age in European universities, in student boarding houses, in the gardens of university towns,
and on the tablecloths of outdoor cafés. Planck, Einstein,
Rutherford, the Curies, de Broglie, Heisenberg, and Bohr
had overthrown the order of physical things, showing that
space and time were only relative concepts, that indivisi-
ble particles could be broken up, that matter itself was

made of something quite intangible that was equivalent to, and perhaps transmutable into, energy. Man's conception of matter changed so fast that Arnold Sommerfeld, professor of physics at the University of Munich, wanted to post a warning at the door of his laboratory: "Caution, Dangerous Structure! Temporarily closed for complete reconstruction." The revolution in physics respected no frontiers. Telegraph clerks the world over, even in Russia, had witnessed sporadic outbursts of strange messages full of incomprehensible formulas announcing the birth of new ideas. Personal letters, scientific papers, and visitors spread the new science the world over, shaking the ground under classical Newtonian physics.

J. Robert Oppenheimer, Landau's elder by four years, then a student in Göttingen and learning the new physics from the very men who had created it, later wrote:

Our understanding of atomic physics, of what we call the quantum theory of atomic systems, had its origin at the turn of the century and its great synthesis and resolutions in the nineteen-twenties. It was a heroic time. It was not the doing of any one man; it involved the collaboration of scores of scientists from many different lands, though from the first to last the deeply creative and subtle and critical spirit of Niels Bohr guided, restrained, deepened, and finally transmuted the enterprise. It was a period of patient work in the laboratory, of crucial experiments and daring action, of many false starts and many untenable conjectures. It was a time of earnest correspondence and hurried conferences, of debate, criticism, and brilliant mathematical improvisation. For those who participated, it was a time of creation; there was terror as well as exaltation in their new insight.

The new physics seeped into a Soviet Union thirsting for contact with Western science. There was, as yet, no secrecy or censorship in scientific research, nor was there the "spy-itis" that was to become epidemic in later years. Marxism itself first took a progressive attitude toward science, overtaking the concepts of French materialistic philosophers. But soon twentieth-century science started to move too fast for the rigid, inflexible tenets of Marxism, which turned out to be incompatible with the subtle, probing, changing spirit of scientific research. It seems that Lenin himself, the genius of the Soviet Revolution, could not understand that science changed its shape like quicksilver. He saw, instead, a "crisis of natural sciences," and maintained that science was threatened not only with idealism (idealism particularly refined, for it tried to use the achievements of science to further itself) but also with agnosticism, the belief that it was not possible to know anything in its essence.

"The new physics," wrote Lenin, "fell into idealism chiefly because physicists did not know dialecticism. . . . They fought for metaphysical materialism, with its mechanicity, and while whipping froth out of the bathtub, they also whipped out the baby" (the baby being, of course, truth). Lenin maintained that modern physics failed because it did not preach the determinism that was essential to Marxism, but preached limited probability instead. Of course there was no way for Lenin to know that in the microworld strict determinism was dead, and limited probability was here to stay.

It is understandable that the uncertainty of the physical world, at a time when thousands upon thousands of Russians were asked to sacrifice their lives for the quasi-religious acceptance of materialistic determinism, was denied and was even regarded as a threat. It is understandable also that uncertainty in physics was viewed only as a transitory stage on the path to proven determinism: Followers of dialectical materialism anticipated the time when spirit and matter could be scientifically linked in a chain of progressive events, for spirit and matter were, after all, one and the same thing. "Lenin's concepts are the highest products of the brain, which itself is the highest product of matter," decreed the editors of the *New Soviet Encyclopedia*, with the almost naïve assurance that was becoming the trademark of the wildest ideological pronouncements.

Nevertheless, when Landau came to Leningrad University in 1924, complete freedom still reigned in the physics department, probably because the politicians were too busy elsewhere. On Vassilevski (St. Basil) Island, in the two hundred-year old building designed by the Swiss architect Trezzini and known as the Twelve Colleges, Lev Landau at first had only passing concern for what ideologists had to say about science. There was enough excitement to be found in physics itself.

The young physicists in Leningrad met at the Borgman Library, a smallish room down a corridor so long that a sign had been jokingly posted to forbid students from riding through it on bicycles. "Uncle Mitya" and "Aunt Sliva," elderly administrators at the university, had been instructed to give the key to the library only to the nine or ten graduate students, but in fact, the room was most frequently occupied by a particularly active and colorful group sometimes referred to as "The Three Musketeers."

Like the heroes of the Dumas novel, the Three Musketeers of Leningrad were four—four close friends, who could not have imagined then how far asunder their destinies would lead them: Lev Landau, a Nobel prize winner-to-be; George Gamow, future exile, leading nuclear theorist, professor in several American universities; "Abatik" Bronstein, destined to meet sudden death at the hands of the secret police; and Dmitri Ivanienko, "the baby" of them all, never to find fame as a scientist, but rather a niche as active defender of "official, Marxist science." In those early years in Leningrad, it was young Ivanienko who gave Landau his nickname, "Dau," a nickname that stuck for life and became known to scientists the world over. "It may be true," remarked Ivanienko one day, "that Landau is an ass. But should he advertise it? *Niet!* I think, therefore, that he should drop *l'âne* [French for ass] from his name, and be charitably called Dau."

The foursome, as befits true musketeers, also had their lady fair, Yevghenia Nikolaievna Kanegiesser, Zhenya to her friends, a younger physics student, perennial *boute-en-train*, writer of topical verse—including the following description of the young physicists at work:

> How snug the Borgman athenaeum!
> For more than five-and-twenty years
> Within this cozy mausoleum
> Young physicists have dried their ears.
>
> Here Ivanienko listens, dozing,
> Sucker in mouth, to ragtime beats,
> While Gamow widely yawns, disclosing
> The countless chocolates he eats.
>
> The band plays on. . . . Landau the clever
> Who'll gladly argue anywhere,
> At any time, with whomsoever,
> Holds a discussion with a chair. . . .

In this stimulating atmosphere of the physics department, neither physics professors Vladimir Fock, Frederiks or Bursian, nor mathematician Krutkov, attempted to impose a rigid discipline upon the group that was so eagerly forging ahead, outdistancing the professors themselves.

Landau, a revolutionary at heart, respected no sacred cows in his personal search for truth. Publishing his first scientific paper at the age of eighteen (on the analysis of spectra of diatomic molecules) he stood out as a somewhat paradoxical figure. His energy and his pugnaciousness were so tremendous that they were often interpreted as stubbornness or insolence, redeemed only by the fact that he was so often right. His opinions constantly defied conventionality. At the same time, he suffered from his awkward appearance and clumsy ways, which gave him a personal fragility which Freud would have attributed to the *Minderwertigkeit* complex, the inferiority complex of daily frustrations. His shyness exasperated him, because shyness itself was irrational and therefore should be rationally eliminated. Landau fought it with assorted weapons, but only with limited success. He would, for instance, become overassertive and aggressive, without any apparent provocation. He accosted strangers in the street: "Could you explain to me why you wear this beard?" he would ask, expounding his argument that beards, and more particularly sideburns, were futile affectations and should be shaved off.

One day his friends spotted him along the Nevski Prospect, the large avenue along the Neva River, where a small crowd was gathering to watch him walking with a red balloon tied to his hat. "Landau, have you gone out of your mind? Why the balloon?" they asked, receiving the cryptic answer that the balloon was worn only to show that if Landau felt like wearing a balloon on the Nevski Prospect, he would wear a balloon on the Nevski Prospect. Another time they saw him sitting on the sidewalk, eating radishes and reading a book, in defiance of the stern glances of passers-by, who found this behavior definitely *ne kulturno*. "What the devil are you doing, Dau?" asked a young student. Landau passed the radishes around. "It is obvious," he answered, "that your faculties of observation will not lead you to great scientific achievement. Anyone can see I am reading a book, and eating radishes."

But often, Landau could not overcome his shyness. He was too timid ever to ask a girl to the theater or to a stroll along the moonlit river. He felt that he was awkward and unattractive, and a refusal would have been too mortifying. To his friends, he explained his lack of active interest in girls otherwise: "You see, I think it is unfair to pick out only the pretty girls to go out with. The ugly ones are hurt when they are left out. On the other hand, I don't like to take out a homely girl, either. So I just don't go out with girls at all."

But when Dau's mind became absorbed, whether in physics or anything else, shyness vanished, replaced by assurance, even cheek. Don Quixote charged ahead, ready to argue for hours, at any time and with anybody.

Understandably, politics and the new state became frequent subjects of discussion among the "young Turks" in Leningrad. Landau had much enthusiasm for the Revolution and a genuine concern for its eventual outcome. He considered himself a true Marxist, spoke his scorn for the *petit bourgeois,* but had grown to mistrust politicians and moralists "who were telling people how they should live." "I have the solution to the problems of the world," he announced one day at the Borgman Library, to the sound of ironic jeers. "Let us call for an International Congress of Moralists. The congress will be held on a ship in the Black Sea, and once the ship is out far enough, it will be sunk. This will solve the problems of the world, by eliminating the people who create them."

Landau viewed with alarm the turn of events after Lenin's death—the rise of Stalin, the strong-armed opposition to Trotsky, the reign of terror and suspicion that seemed so useless. The Three Musketeers no doubt passed through varying shades of political opinion, but at one time, the group was described by one of its members as divided into four distinct factions: Ivanienko the anarchist, Landau the Trotskyist, and Gamow the opportunist, who didn't care about politics, but only about physics. The fourth, Bronstein, might have been something of an idealist but, "in the end of ends"—as the Russian saying goes—he wasn't given the chance of making up his mind.

The young physicists received small scholarships or stipends from the government. They lived if not in misery, at least in very Spartan circumstances, sometimes holding several jobs at the same time—teaching at the university, working at the Radium Institute in a building that had once been an asylum, at the Optical Institute across from the Physics department, or at the Physics-Technical Roentgen Institute created by Professor Abraham Yoffe (known as Papa Yoffe), way out on Leningrad's outskirts, under Professor Yakov Frenkel.

Landau, who was never preoccupied with money, probably had more at his disposal than his friends. He lived at his aunt's home, received pocket money from his parents in Baku, and a government research scholarship at the Roentgen Institute.

George Gamow, Dau's elder by four years, the grandson of a Czarist general and of a metropolitan in the

Orthodox Church (a genealogy which he did not publicize) had grander tastes and at one time held as many as five jobs, including a colonelcy in the Soviet Army, in which he acted as instructor, and as a keeper of meteorological records so far out of town that commuting was one of his chief problems. Gamow, who spent much of his time standing in line to receive his various salaries every other week, had so much trouble making ends meet that when he lost his pince-nez, he could be seen peering ahead with his finger pressed to his eyeball, deforming the lens in order to achieve a clearer focus of vision while saving up for a new pair of glasses.

Snacks to keep long sessions going at the Borgman Library had to be frugal, and chocolates for Gamow weren't always on the menu. Bread at 10 kopecks a pound was accessible, but the traditional Russian salted cucumbers, at 39 kopecks, had to be rationed. Beer, too, was rather a luxury: workers paid 25 kopecks a pint, but the charge for "intellectuals" was 40 kopecks. The young physicists could afford inexpensive theater tickets, but often wrote, produced, and acted in their own sketches and revues, whose characters strangely resembled many physicists of world renown. They even published a "scientific journal," *PhysikalischeDummheiten* (physical nonsense) in which both healthy and "pathological" physics were freely commented upon.

The chief commodity, however, was free of charge. Avidly, they learned the new science, the subject of countless seminars with Bursian, Yoffe, Fock, and Frenkel, with visiting foreign physicists, seminars during which Landau usually stood out as the most brilliant and the most vocal participant. At the same time, the young physicists shared the same ambition: to study in Göttingen or

Copenhagen, in Cambridge, Berlin, or Zurich, where the makers of quantum physics could be seen, heard, talked to. Several Russian physicists had already been abroad, returning with first-hand stories about Einstein, Niels Bohr, Wolfgang Pauli or Sir Ernest Rutherford. Russian physicist Piotr Kapitza had practically become a Britisher since 1921, spending most of his time in Cambridge, returning home for summer holidays. In Leningrad, then the center of Soviet science, no reward was more coveted than a government scholarship abroad, or a fellowship grant from the Rockefeller Foundation.

Gamow was the first to go. "Well, comrades," he smugly announced one day in the spring of 1928, "I'm afraid I'll have to leave you to your petty occupations! The fatherland, discerning in me the most promising of its physicists, has asked me to travel abroad to represent Soviet science. How can I refuse?" Buoyant and debonair, the tall youth boarded the train to Berlin, wearing a pair of bizarre white trousers, probably the only unpatched ones in his possession. Raging, Dau stayed behind. His repeated requests to leave the country, if only for the summer holidays, were denied. Wrote Genia Kanegiesser on a postcard mailed to Gamow in Göttingen:

You didn't check your milk-white slacks?
You're hopeless, Geo! . . . Dau raved and ranted
And looked about for rope and ax
Because his passport wasn't granted.

But now he yields to his defeat
(And boils with inner irritation),
Plays tennis in the August heat,
And sails the Volga on vacation . . .

Landau indeed sailed to the southern resort of Tiber-
dah, returning in the fall to apply his stubborn energy to
physics—and to making the trip abroad. His teachers recommended him both to Soviet authorities and to the
Rockefeller Foundation officials as Russia's brightest
young physicist. Their esteem for Dau is reflected in the
letters Professor Frenkel wrote to the Rockefeller Foundation in November 1928 and February 1929:

At the age of 19 he [Landau] was graduated from the University of Leningrad and for the last two years has been working at the Physics-Technical Roentgen Institute on various
questions of quantum mechanics. In spite of his youth (he is at
present only 21 years of age) he is one of the best specialists in
this subject to which he has already given a few contributions
of great interest and importance (the last one is a generaliza-
tion of Dirac's theory of the electron for the case of a multi-
electronic system).

I am *perfectly sure* that Landau will prove at once one of
the most brilliant fellows of the Rockefeller Foundation. In
fact I never met with a young man of his age with so much
talent and depth of thought.

Prof. Born [this referred to Max Born, then Professor of
Theoretical Physics at the University of Göttingen] during his
recent visit to Russia has himself uttered his desire to accept
Landau as foreign student at his Göttingen Institute.

I am perfectly sure that you will get the best impression of
him. To my opinion Mr. Landau deserves a fellowship more
than anyone else in this country.

Finally, the dream came true, in all of its splendor. In
October 1929 Narkompross—the People's Commission on
Education—selected Landau for a Soviet government

traveling fellowship. This was to be followed by a Rocke-feller Fellowship covering tuition, laboratory and equipment fees, travel, and some living expenses. Both were to add up to a year-and-a-half abroad.

When twenty-one-year-old Dau left Leningrad, he had already done significant work in quantum mechanics of molecules, quantum statistics, radiation damping in the quantum theory, quantum theory of the spinning electron, and was very probably the Soviet Union's most brilliant physicist. His stay abroad was to make him one of the world's leading theoreticians.

CHAPTER 3

Exploring
a New World

(OCTOBER 1929–MARCH 1931)

THERE was so much to do, so much to learn and so many people to see in the European universities and physics institutes that Landau sat in the train taking him across the Soviet border through Poland and into Germany with as much trepidation as a hungry child about to be set loose in a pastry shop. His striking figure, clad in old, outlandish clothes, first appeared in October 1929 in Göttingen, where he was promptly advised to secure a fresher suit and was directed to the Pension Wunderlich, a favorite abode for the physicists who, year after year, crowded into this Mecca of quantum physics.

Since 1807, when Carl Friedrich Gauss became lecturer in mathematics and director of the Göttingen observatory, this small town in central Germany had become famous as a manufacturing center for mathematicians, as well as for sausages and beer. Already in the nineteenth century, Gaussian mathematics were paving the way for relativistic, curved space-time concepts, and in the 1920s the town was a nucleus around which quantum physicists spun like electrons in the newly-discovered excited state.

Since 1921 Max Born, the son of a biologist and himself a graduate of the Mathematical Institute of Göttingen's Georgia Augusta University (that was becoming known as the Nobel Prize university) had been teaching at the Second Physics Institute, an ugly red brick building well known to at least two generations of physicists the world over. Born (who was to receive the Nobel Prize in 1954), mathematician David Hilbert, and physicist James Franck (already a Nobel laureate), started a new type of school of physics, in which they were not only teaching but trying to solve, with their students and with the foreign physicists that constantly appeared at their seminars, the problems of quantum physics.

During a visit to Leningrad Max Born had already met Landau, was favorably impressed by the clarity and purposefulness of his mind, and invited him to drop in. From the moment Landau arrived in Göttingen, still speaking a somewhat Slavic brand of German, he acquired the reputation of a perennial and reckless volunteer who jumped up, as if he were motivated by some inner-coil spring, to answer almost any question, unless someone with a more rapid muscular reaction had preceded him.

After a few weeks in Göttingen, Landau trekked to Leipzig to attend classes under twenty-nine-year-old Werner Heisenberg, one of the creators of quantum physics and the originator of the Heisenberg Uncertainty Principle. Heisenberg had been named a professor at Leipzig at the age of twenty-six, and was soon to receive the Nobel Prize for work he had done at twenty-five. Landau's stay in Leipzig was brief, but punctuated by many vehement discussions with the man whose concepts helped topple physical determinism that was taken for granted only a few years earlier. From Leipzig, Landau traveled to Denmark.

It was in Copenhagen that Landau found the one mind that was to be his guide in future years: that of Niels Bohr, the illustrious creator of "Bohr's atom," the leading spirit who, probably more than anyone else, contributed to the coherent crystallization of the strange discoveries of quantum physics.

It was the winter of 1929 when Landau's striking figure stalked into the rather conservative surroundings of the Universitets Institut for Teoretisk Fysik on 15 Blegdamsvej, asking for Herr Niels Bohr. "What a strange mailman," someone commented, taking in the gawky youth who was wearing a bright red blazer.

Niels Bohr was then forty-four years old. A graduate of the University of Copenhagen, he had worked at Cambridge University under Sir J. J. Thomson, and with Sir Ernest Rutherford at the University of Manchester. Expanding ideas formulated in Max Planck's quantum theory of radiation, which showed that atoms acquired and lost energy not in a continuous manner, but in definite "quantum jumps," Bohr formulated the principle of the quantum theory of the atom in the clearest possible form, pointing out that these principles could not be understood from the point of view of classical physics, but required a new approach to the concept of causality and physical determinism. Bohr had been awarded the Nobel Prize in physics, continuing his work at the Copenhagen University's Institute for Theoretical Physics, built for his research. In 1928, a year before Landau's arrival in Copenhagen, Bohr had formulated his "principle of complementarity" and studied its implications not only for physics, but for man's concept of his world, and for the philosophical thought of modern times.

Complementarity was developed, in essence, to reconcile principles of quantum physics that were irrational from the viewpoint of classical physics, yet that could not be explained without reference to the latter. Namely, it had become apparent that radiation, which in some of its manifestations could only be formulated clearly in terms of waves, had to be viewed sometimes as if it consisted of particles. These two faces of radiation gave rise to equations that were paradoxical to each other, yet that were necessary to explain its characteristics. As Leon Rosenfeld, one of Bohr's students and Landau's friend, described it later:

What we meet with here is actually a problem of logic. . . . The new logical instrument which was created by Bohr is called complementarity. Complementarity denotes the logical relation, of quite a new type, between concepts which are mutually exclusive, and which therefore cannot be considered at the same time because that would lead to logical mistakes, but which nevertheless must both be used to give a complete description of the situation. . . .

Rosenfeld wrote further:

In classical physics, "the expression of causality is the result of the mathematical properties of equations expressing the laws of motion of particles and of propagation of the electromagnetic field. . . . When we are given the initial conditions . . . the solution of the equation is completely determined: And accordingly, the type of causality of classical physics is determinism. This is no longer the case when we have a complementarity relationship.

In other words, in the concepts of classical physics the precise description of a situation would enable the observer to predict with precision its outcome, and if no prediction were made, it was only because the means to obtain such a precise description were not, for the time being, available. But the principle of uncertainty formulated by Werner Heisenberg and expanded by Bohr showed that one cannot even hope to speak of all physical quantities with unlimited accuracy: The very observation of an atom is enough to disturb it. Deterministic causality was replaced with limited probability.

A profound thinker, Bohr was not an authoritarian, nor was he really a pedagogue. Rather than teaching, he worked *with* his students and steered them in the right direction when they erred, creating the kind of equalitarian relationship that was undoubtedly the least strenuous way to run a social group consisting of physicists, who are not, by and large, people easy to live with. If the institute was a patriarchal organization, Bohr was an indulgent father to a large number of more or less well-behaved *Wunderkinder*, to whom he gave complete freedom to run about and get themselves into theoretical mischief.

Bohr did not like to hurt anybody's feelings, even one's whose work had been worthless. Any new idea was usually greeted as "magnificent," and it was only later that the author might find out, through well-directed criticism that frequently took the form of questions, that he was far off course. If Bohr did not immediately qualify an effort as magnificent but received it with a comment such as "Ah, this is very, very interesting," then the author could be fairly certain that his work was no good at all.

It is perhaps because Bohr did not expect formal demonstrations of respect to his seniority and position that he was the more respected. No doubt he appreciated this, among other reasons because it gave him an edge in the endless discussions with members of his flock. Bohr was a poor speaker, mixing up his German, Danish, and English in sentences that were sometimes blurred, and in the long talking marathons with Landau, he even picked up a few Russian words which he released in moments of excitement.

Landau remained a tireless talker and even if his arguments did not convince, he often succeeded in drowning his opponent in a torrent of words. Against Dau, Bohr frequently applied one of his favorite delaying techniques, which required undeniable talent and a certain training: If Dau came up with an argument that Bohr could not immediately answer, though he felt intuitively that something was wrong with it, Bohr would start talking about an entirely irrelevant matter, hoping that Landau would have the courtesy not to interrupt him. This usually worked, and as he talked, Bohr prepared his real argument which he would suddenly spring upon his astonished student, giving him the complete analysis of a question formulated only a few minutes earlier.

These exotic fellows from Russia, Dau and Gamow (the latter had found his way to Copenhagen during the latest Bohr Festival Season) were well accepted in Bohr's group, much liked for their charm, sense of humor, liberalism, and freedom of expression that were refreshing in an atmosphere which was endowed with a certain amount of Danish conservatism. Bohr particularly liked Landau, who in turn has ever since considered himself a student of Bohr, and not of anybody else he studied under. Yet the two were in thorough disagreement on more subjects

than they could agree upon, even outside of physics. Politically Bohr was rather conservative, while Landau believed Marxism was the hope of the world. Bohr was
religious, while Landau was completely atheistic and considered religion as a useless convention. Even their tastes
in literature were far apart, and if Bohr said he liked Schil-
ler's *Sayings of Confucius*, Landau scorned it as bourgeois. As an example of what poetry should be like,
Landau once started reciting a poem from *Intermezzo* by
Heinrich Heine, about the sorrow of unrequited love;
Wolfgang Pauli, who happened to be nearby and had
heard Landau's remarks about "bourgeois literature," listened with a sarcastic smile as Dau went on describing
the fair lady's pearly teeth and sapphire eyes. "To put it in
a few words," concluded Pauli, "you like it so that each
part of the body is a mineral, no?"

Landau and Bohr also strongly disagreed about many
aspects of quantum physics. Dau reproached Bohr for
philosophizing too much and one day, when Bohr left the
library after talking to his students about the philosophical implications of complementarity, Landau dramatically
threw up his spiderlike arms in protest: "Has Bohr given
up physics?"

Bohr's students lived in boardinghouses, the favorite
being Miss Have's and Miss Thalbitzer's. Landau,
Gamow, and Rosenfeld stayed at Miss Have's small pension on the Blegdamsvej Triangle, not far from the institute—and almost part of it. Work often went on late at
night in the dining room, to the accompaniement of tea
and crackers served by Froken Have, who was so proud of
"her physicists" that she felt like one herself, and occasionally proposed a theory of her own. Miss Have's pension was a warm home for Landau, who would often in-

vite physicists into his small room to continue late into the night a discussion started elsewhere. The popularity enjoyed by Miss Have was in no way diminished by the fact that she seemed to have a large collection of nieces, who in turn had many girl friends, all of them being invited to an occasional party organized by the aunt. She was so liked by the physicists she lodged and fed that when she moved a few years later to a less convenient location, all those who had remained in Copenhagen faithfully followed her.

At the pension, Landau expounded his opinions not only about physics, but again about all of his favorite subjects, delighted when he could shock people with his ideas which were rapidly becoming known as part of the "Landau Theoretical-Physical approach to life." The opinions themselves became known as "records," which Landau would "spin" at the slightest excuse. (Later, his students in Moscow even compiled a "Dictionary of Landau Records.")

The opinions included such generalites as "Men don't like to study, but they like to work; women would study all their lives, if only given a chance," or "Women don't make good physicists, not because they don't have the brains, but because they worry too much about other things." Or more precise likes and dislikes, such as his perennial phobia of whiskers. Beards even became the objects of games, statistical studies, and bets. Physicist Rudolph Peierls remembers making one such bet with Landau; the wager had to do with the proportion of bearded men in Russia versus elsewhere. Its exact terms have now been forgotten, but Peierls recalls that Landau lost.

Dau's former Copenhagen colleagues still remember a particularly entertaining episode that took place when a young medical student appeared at Miss Have's board-inghouse wearing a neatly trimmed beard. Throughout the dinner Landau squirmed on his chair and after dessert, he stood up and introduced himself, no longer able to resist bringing up his pet arguments against beards in the hope of persuading the student to shave. "Begging your pardon, do you not think there is a barber around?" he said, and rambled on with his views about the uselessness of whiskers and the desirability of having them trimmed. Bewildered, the student looked up at him, failing to un-derstand the point and taking in the unruly, wavy, abun-dant shock of dark hair looming over him. "Why, of course," he said, smiling, and proceeded to indicate to the scarlet-faced Landau the way to the nearest barber shop.

Landau seldom discussed politics, except among close friends. In Leningrad, he had been suspected of Trot-skyism, but when abroad, he read Trotsky's work, which was now banned in the Soviet Union, and was disap-pointed. He was none too happy with the Stalin dictator-ship, but considered himself a "true Leninist and Marxist," whatever this represented. (Once, when he ex-perienced difficulties in obtaining a visa to return to Zur-ich, he commented rather proudly, "Didn't they allow Lenin to live in Switzerland? Could it be that they have realized I am a more dangerous revolutionary than Lenin himself?")

For Gamow and Landau Leningrad's Borgman Library was advantageously replaced by the library at Niels Bohr's institute, where physicists gathered to work and play. The large working table occasionally doubled-up for ping-pong, and the blackboard was usually covered with figures and symbols that were erased only with due caution. Gamow had started working on physics of the atomic nucleus, a field in which he was to acquire world fame, while Landau tackled any subject, often acting as a more vehement critic and judge than Bohr himself, who joined the discussions every day.

Working with Rudolph Peierls, Dau started exploring, among other things, quantum electrodynamics, in which the pair pointed out some existing inconsistencies that gave hints for a completely new approach to the subject. In a lighter vein, Landau also developed his "Mathematical Theory of Love," which enabled the determination, with a presumably high degree of statistical probability, of the chances for two people to fall in love. In the method, which was actually tested on a few physicists and their Danish girl friends, a person would be characterized by a *psi* function, which would be developed with respect to his physical and intellectual attributes. The characteristics of a person, expertly plotted on the abcissa, actually enabled a trained theorist to recognize the person in question. The method of determining amorous compatibility consisted of taking a man's *psi* function, multiplying it by a universal factor, and conjugating it with the *psi* function of a lady. The result was integrated, and actually gave a probability which was called the probability of love. The Mathematical Theory of Love was so ingeniously developed that it even took into consideration who would fall in love first, and how the other party would respond: the probability was reached through noncommutative algebra, the kind that can be briefly described by stating that A times B is not necessarily equal to B times A. There was also the Landau Coefficient of Beauty, a useful tool for statistical studies comparing the relative proportions of feminine beauty in various countries or in different sections of Copenhagen. In these mathematical exercises,

Landau was chiefly the theorist, while Gamow tended toward experimental physics.

From Copenhagen, where two months of intensive work had considerably increased his intellectual baggage, Landau returned to Germany to attend Heisenberg's seminars in Leipzig, then traveled to Cambridge to study under Paul Dirac, "the mystic of the atom," as lanky and ethereal as the famed Dirac delta function itself. Dirac, then twenty-eight years old, was usually so deeply plunged in figures and symbols that ran through his mind or that he lined up along the blackboard, that he could seldom comment upon them in down-to-earth words. Physicists working with him used to say that "Dirac utters a sentence only about once every light year."

The four-month stay in Cambridge was Landau's first assignment sponsored by the Rockefeller Foundation, and there again he met Gamow, who had also received a fellowship from the Rockefeller Foundation, to study at Cambridge under Rutherford, the sixty-year-old veteran of modern physics.

George Gamow, who always had so many ideas that he couldn't screen them all himself, frequently received Landau's assistance, nimbly to review or develop formulas concerned with the analysis of the atomic nucleus. In the summer of 1930, Gamow took Dau along on a motorcycle tour of England. To this day Gamow remembers the trip, which took them to Scotland, following an itinerary established by Landau, who wanted to visit a number of art galleries and exhibits to satisfy a newly acquired interest in art: Gamow's muscular frame bouncing with ease on the comfortable driver's seat, and Landau's bony consitution suffering from the potholes which he tried to avoid by leaning right or left to steer the oblivious driver away from them.

At Cambridge, Landau still held forth with vigor, though perhaps a year in the midst of the great had given him a humility he did not earlier possess. In physics, he did not feel any longer the strong need to assert himself, as he often did in his social relationships. Scientists, like everybody else, can grow up with a natural competitiveness that drives them to assert their superiority in their field of endeavor. Sometimes this drive can persist to their last breath, sometimes it can become extinguished or moderated for a variety of reasons, ranging from the endless puncturing of the ego by repeated frustrations, to a more quiet and fruitful realization and acceptance of one's own capabilities. Only to the most fortunate of them does this moderation come about simply because they have reached the top, a position which they share in a comfortable and friendly manner with their peers. If Landau realized that he had reached the top, it was without cocky presumption, but rationally, by measuring himself against the people he admired most.

To the physicists around him, the fact that he had reached the top was already apparent when Landau, leaving Cambridge, arrived in Zurich to work with Wolfgang Pauli. There again he met Peierls and Rosenfeld who were working with another young physicist, Bloch, on quantum physics problems concerned with metals—"metals were in fashion at that time" remembers Rosenfeld.

Landau had never tackled the subject, coming in "cold." He sat in during conversations and debates, listened, asked a few pointed questions and, a week later, astounded his colleagues by coming up with the complete solution to the problem of diamagnetism, one of Dau's most significant findings, referred to ever since as "Landau's diamagnetism." The other physicists started talking with great animation, and soon it sounded as if it were they, rather than Landau, who had developed the solution. Only later did Dau speak up to comment, "Well, fellows, after all, I hope you still remember that you are talking about the method *I* have just come up with!"

Landau had grown, but maturity did not mean that he became any more conservative, or that he lost any of his pugnaciousness. It did mean, however, a more studied, orderly manner in his work. "If you want to solve a problem, you think hard about it right from the bottom up," he would say, and in this manner he tackled anything that came up, challenging subjects caught in a conversation or "spontaneous" problems that dawned upon him at the most unexpected time (as seems to be the tradition with physicists). He would attack them from the basic, first principles, and usually work his way through.

Less than ever was he impressed by sacred cows. "It's not *who* says it, it's *what* he says," he would remark, when someone tried to give strength to a theory because it came from a "big physicist." Dau may have admired Einstein's work on relativity, for instance, but he criticized him for trying to develop a theory of fields that would replace quantum theories (a criticism eventually shared by a majority of scientists). Once after a lecture, a reporter approached a group of physicists, asking them what was the difference in the understanding of the uncertainty principle between Wolfgang Pauli and a prominent philosopher who had spoken at the meeting. The young physicists hesitated, but Landau plunged right in: "The big difference," he said, "is that Pauli understands the principle of uncertainty, and Professor X doesn't."

Maturity did not mean, either, that he no longer could be carried away with an enthusiasm that some considered excessive. In Zurich, he still deluged Pauli with arguments that left both of them breathless. "Now, Dr. Pauli, you've got to admit that not *all* I've said is nonsense," once protested Dau, seeing the Viennese scientist hopelessly shaking his head. Retorted Pauli: "What you have said is so confused I couldn't even tell whether it was wrong or not!"

One of the most telling comments about Dau's status as a physicist when he had nearly exhausted his Rockefeller Fellowship time came from his colleague and friend, Rudolph Peierls (who was later to become the husband of the Leningrad physics student and versifier Genia Kanegiesser). Said Peierls, one day after Landau left a conference room in Zurich after making a particularly penetrating analysis of some aspects of magnetism: "Friends, let's face it. We are living from the crumbs of Landau's table."

February 1931 was, for Lev Davidovich Landau, the time to make a decision he knew would have momentous consequences for his future. Should he, now, return to the Soviet Union?

Since his first days in Berlin, when he was given two pairs of shoes and wondered aloud, "Who can possibly need two pairs of shoes?", since he begged his colleagues not to discuss politics in public with him, for such discussions had ways of seeping back home, Landau knew well that life in Western Europe would be easier, more free and carefree, than in the Soviet Union where Stalin, the man he despised, was now in full power. Here also Landau's life might be more fruitful, for it is here that the finishing touches were now being applied to the new physics. Here, the restless intellectual activities of the international set of physicists who freely roamed through European universities represented a powerful stimulus.

The many arguments that must have come to Dau's mind, weighing the balance to one side or the other, have now been forgotten. But it would seem that Landau's "Theoretical-Physics approach to life," the studied, rational façade presented to the world, did not provide the strongest motive. If Dau were going back to Russia, it would be because his loyalty, his heart were there. It would be because he was, himself, a revolutionary at heart.

There could be no question, however, of going back home without returning once more to his teacher and guide, Niels Bohr. As a matter of fact, a ready-made excuse was on hand for him to visit Copenhagen: Landau and Peierls had just undertaken an important work, which had to be discussed with Bohr. The Rockefeller Fellowship had run out, so had money from home; but somehow Dau managed to scrape up enough for the trip. (The grants given by the Rockefeller and other foundations, it seems, were not always used by the physicists in complete accordance with the foundation's rules and wishes. "Our records are not quite clear on this point," notes a Rockefeller Foundation official, "but it seems that the fellowship [Landau's] was originally intended to cover study at Cambridge and Zurich, and at Leipzig under Professor W. Heisenberg. . . . At what time Professor Bohr's laboratory was added to his plans we cannot tell." Another slight violation is clearly remembered by Gamow, who had to submit a medical certificate from Russia before receiving

approval of his grant. As Gamow happened to be somewhere down south at the time, he arranged for a lady
friend of his, who was a physician, to sign a form which
he later filled out himself, making a serious enough mis-
take to receive it back with the terse comment that if
the answers were correct, then Gamow must be on his
deathbed.)

In a book about Niels Bohr and the development of
quantum physics, Professor Leon Rosenfeld precedes his
chapter on quantum electrodynamics with a recollection
of Dau's last visit to Copenhagen:

When I arrived at the Institute on the last day of February,
1931, for my annual stay, the first person I saw was Gamow. I
asked him about the news, he replied in his own picturesque
way by showing me a neat pen drawing he had just made. It
represented Landau, tightly bound to a chair and gagged,
while Bohr, standing before him with upraised forefinger, was
saying, "*Bitte, bitte, Landau, muss ich noch ein Wort sagen?*"
(This was Bohr's slight Danishism for the German meaning
"Please, please, Landau, may I put in another word?") I
learned that Landau and Peierls had just come a few days
before with some new paper of theirs which they wanted to
show Bohr, "but," (Gamow added airily) "he does not seem to
agree. And this is the kind of discussion which has been going
on all the time."

Peierls had left the day before "in a state of complete ex-
haustion," Gamow said. Landau stayed for a few weeks longer,
and I had the opportunity of ascertaining that Gamow's representation of the situation was only exaggerated to the extent
usually conceded to artistic fantasy.

When Landau left Copenhagen a few days later, he had
the feeling that he might not be able to return for a long
time. "But I have to work for my country," he told Rosen-

feld. "This is a long good-bye. Perhaps forever, unless it is you who come to visit me."

Today, Rosenfeld remembers Landau as a true friend, possessing qualities that become particularly apparent in difficult moments. "Behind a sarcastic veneer, a façade of brashness that may have been a form of protection, Landau was fundamentally a good and very kind person," says Rosenfeld. "He is one of the finest persons I have ever known."

CHAPTER 4

Physics
and the Commissars

(1931–1938)

WHEN Landau returned to Leningrad in 1931, a change in the Soviet government's attitude toward its scientists had become noticeable.

Only a few years earlier scientists and scientific students, though receiving substantial state support, were left free to a degree that bordered on anarchy. In the decade that followed the Revolution, a merciless struggle for power kept politicians too busy to give much thought to reconciling science and political philosophy. The new state was also concerned with obtaining recognition from the West. Foreign travel for deserving scientists was favorably looked upon, invitations to foreign laboratories were taken as compliments, and when the Rockefeller Foundation selected a Russian for one of its fellowships, Soviet national pride was boundless.

Now it became less and less tolerable that Soviet citizens engaged in the pursuit of scientific achievement took no active interest in politics. Increasing political and ideological support was demanded from scientists— particularly in physics and biology, two disciplines where the current trends could be interpreted as going against "the victorious tides of dialectical materialism."

In physics, the threat came from recent work by Bohr and Heisenberg, which led to the conclusion that a strict determinism did not exist on the atomic level; Complementarity in particular was termed a deviationist, bourgeois concept, because it could be seen casting some doubt on the determinism of events taking place on a larger scale. And in biology, the development of Mendelian genetics led Western scientists to agree that only those traits inherited from one's parents could be passed on to one's offspring, while acquired characters or learned behavior were not hereditary. This was not compatible with the Marxist ideal of reforming humanity by subjecting it, for the required number of generations, to appropriate environmental pressures.

Countless mice in the Soviet Union underwent the amputation of their tails in the futile hope that after several generations of this treatment, a tail-less mouse would be born to the world. When this and similar experiments consistently failed, some scientists started cheating. As their results now corresponded to the Marxist ideal, they were rewarded with scientifically undeserved advancement and comfortably settled down to corrupt Soviet biology for several decades. Most venomous among these "Marxist geneticists" was Trofim Denisovich Lysenko, a plant breeder rather than a scientifically trained geneticist, who became and remained for many years the dictator of Soviet biology. Lysenko was Stalin's "teacher's pet," and a deviation from Lysenkoism was so dangerous that several scientists—notably the famous Nikolai Vavilov—were jailed and executed for their Mendelian views.

Some of the politico-scientific pronouncements, expounded in the Soviet Union with dead-pan seriousness, were so preposterous that they would deserve only to be laughed at, if they hadn't had tragic consequences at the same time. Both modern physics and genetics were termed "dangerous idealism"; even worse, they were "ecclesiastical," giving fuel to the Church in its aim to plunge the world into "total obscurantism." Bohr was accused of purposely distorting physics to serve bourgeois ideas. George Gamow, who returned to Russia in 1931, shortly after Landau, described the situation in a somewhat Russified English, and with his own brand of humor.

"The problem of the stability and disintegration of atomic nuclei could not be solved on the basis of idealistic conceptions worked out by the governing class of capitalists and their valets and it was necessary the fresh stream of dialectic reasoning to find the real basis of radioactive phenomena," Gamow observed. "The popularity of these uncertainty ideas between the bourgeois physicists is mainly due to a big advertising organized by Danish physicist N. Bohr whose idealistic tendencies are well known to everyone familiar with the question. . . . Willing or nonwilling one must feel that the only way for the farther investigation of the treasury of nature and its utilization for the benefit of the working class is shown by the dialectic philosophy of the winning proletariat."

Like Gamow, many Russian physicists thought all this was pretty funny, until their knuckles were severely rapped by Soviet officialdom, which resembles other bureaucratic organizations at least in that it is notably devoid of any sense of humor. Yaroslav Frenkel, Landau's former teacher and director of the Leningrad Physics-Technical Institute in the bucolic setting of pine woods at the east end of the city, discovered this shortage when he delivered a popular lecture describing the theory that radiation must sometimes be considered as particles, sometimes as waves. "Of course, in our conception, these two alternatives exclude each other," he commented airily. "So, comrades, you should believe in particles on Mondays, Wednesdays, and Fridays, and in waves on Tuesdays, Thursdays, and Saturdays."

Soviet authorities, who probably had little idea that Frenkel had described an actual paradox of quantum physics, took him to task for being a reactionary and spreading bourgeois propaganda. For this and other sins Frenkel, one of Russia's ablest physicists and teachers, who was later to become instrumental in the development of Soviet nuclear weapons, was chastised in no uncertain terms by the *Great Soviet Encyclopedia,* that ubiquitous mouthpiece of the powers that be.

"The philosophical ideas of Ja. L. Frenkel are not notable for their clarity and consistency insofar as his attitude to materialism is concerned," the entry under his name declared. "Many of the statements in his books suffer directly or indirectly from idealist distortion and have been rightly subjected to strong criticism by the community of Soviet scientists."

Landau himself, a year after his return to Leningrad where he took up research at the Physics-Technical Institute and teaching at the university, fell afoul of the commissars.

One day in the spring of 1932, Dau was sitting in the

Borgman Library, leafing through the latest volume of the *Great Soviet Encyclopedia,* which had just been published and delivered to the Physics Department. Gamow was having a discussion with two younger students, and "Abatik" Bronstein had walked into the room, when Landau waved a bony hand. *"Noo-ka, tovarishchi!* Listen to this!"

What had attracted his attention was the encyclopedia entry for ETHER. It had been written by one B. Gessen, a Moscow physicist whose renown came less from his ability as a scientist than from his attitude as a fervent supporter of Marxist views upon the natural sciences. To this day the text remains as a historic example of the type of nonsense that is written when science is viewed through an ideological bias, rivaling some of the more aberrant arguments presented during the Mississippi "monkey trial" of Darwinism.

Landau began to read aloud:

"As experiments by Michelson* did not give the possibility of determining the velocities of bodies in relation to ether, so the special theory of relativity declares ether to be non-existent. The theory refuses, therefore, to answer the question of objectivity of physical events.

"Likewise, from the theory of J. J. Thomson, there results an unavoidable consequence: that ether must be contained, confined along its boundaries, otherwise it would gather at one point, like an unconfined soap bubble. It becomes incomprehensible then, how in the face of infinity, ether can be confined. In modern physics the strictly phenomenological views about ether still prevail; these views in effect deny its existence.

"The basis of the methodological error of the general

---

* Albert A. Michelson (1852-1931) experimentally determined the velocity of light.

theory of relativity is that it considers ether as an absolutely uninterrupted medium, while all modern theories on the structure of matter (quantum theory, wave mechanics) increasingly tend to confirm the position of dialectical materialism which holds that matter in its objective structure is at the same time continued, and discontinued. But modern theories in their present form have a certain degree of mathematical formalism. . . . So that the problem of ether in modern physics is only posed, but far from solved, even in a general way . . ."

As the reading of Gessen's analysis of the predicaments of ether went on, merriment in the Borgman Library was such that Landau held up a long forefinger, asking for silence. "Wait, please wait . . . The best is yet to come!" He continued with the *Encyclopedia* entry:

"We often find in physics a completely false representation of the ether of matter. Engels, in *Dialectics of Nature,* speaks of ether, saying that 'if it exists at all then it must be material, it must fall within the understanding of matter.'

"Taking heavy and inert mass as the only criterion of materiality, physicists tended to deny the materiality of ether, as ether does not have weight or inertia. Here we have that mixture of physical and philosophical conception of matter, of which Lenin made a penetrating analysis, studying the crisis of physics at the beginning of the twentieth century. Ether is a particular quality of matter, and physics is only approaching the study of its properties. Ether does not have an objective reality, as other material bodies do. From this viewpoint, denying ether is senseless and leads to agnostic and idealistic conclusions."

Slowly laughter in the Borgman Library subsided, recurring now and then when a particularly entertaining passage was quoted again. Gamow sat down and started drawing one of the childish, satirical cartoons for which he had already become famous.

The cartoon (is it still filed today deep in the red-taped records so cherished by Soviet bureaucracy?) represented a garbage can, chock-full of assorted trash such as relativity, phlogiston ("combustible spirit" fancied by eighteenth-century alchemists), quantum physics, and a bottle of pharmaceutical ether. On the lid that was perched askew on top of the can there sat a cat, beaming with satisfaction; the cat bore a striking resemblance to "physicist" Gessen.

Landau, Gamow, and Bronstein then joined forces to coauthor their own article about ether, noting among other things that ether was in point of fact so undeniably material that it was a liquid filling insterstellar space, through which it might be possible to swim if ether didn't have such strong soporific properties; that to deny phlogiston was dangerously agnostic and could lead to the explosion of physical sciences, as if they were an unconfined soap bubble. The trio signed their names to the article, and the two young students insisted on signing too. All gaily ambled to the nearest postoffice and dispatched their satirical masterpiece, together with Gamow's cartoon, to the editors of the *Great Soviet Encyclopedia* in Moscow.

A few weeks later, when they had all but forgotten this cheerful episode, the news came from Leningrad Party Headquarters that Gamow, Landau, Bronstein, and the two students were to remain in town, pending trial for reactionary activities. The trial was to be held at the university as soon as a committee of political commissars was available for that purpose. Gamow nevertheless managed to find a valid excuse to travel south, and only Dau, Bronstein, and the two students stood trial. "Papa" Yoffe, who had been summoned to testify about the activities and opinions of the young physicists, also left Leningrad for the urgent matter of attending the funeral of a cousin.

It is unfortunate that no records of the trial have been made public. The situation was apparently saved by Bronstein, who insisted that he and the other accused were in fact ardent Marxists, who spurned reactionary physics as much as anybody else. The incident, he apologized, was a mere youthful prank, which they honestly regretted now. Needless to say, the joke was not appreciated by the stern jury. Landau, Gamow (found guilty *in absentia*), and Bronstein temporarily lost their teaching jobs, as it was feared they might corrupt the young students at the university. They were allowed to keep their research appointments, with a warning not to make stupid and childish jokes about such serious matters as dialectical materialism. The two students who had signed their names to the spoof were expelled from the university; Gamow does not remember seeing them in Leningrad again. Later Gamow wrote an earnest, long letter to Stalin himself; he wrote that he was thoroughly familiar both with dialectical materialism and with relativity and modern physics, and tried to explain that neither had anything to do with nor anything to fear from the other.

At the end of 1932, both Landau and Gamow again applied for permission to travel abroad, as they had standing invitations from several institutes. Permission was denied.

It was denied again the following year, and in the summer of 1933 Dau and George traveled north to Khibini, near Murmansk, where a rest and study base had been made available to physicists by the K.S.U., the Committee of Assistance to Students. The "base" in fact consisted of an isolated shack with neither water nor electricity; Dau and Gamow were its only occupants, thoroughly enjoying their vacation, reading, hiking, and holding forth about the future of physics—and their own future.

The K.S.U. base turned out to be the site of the only scientific work that was to be copublished by Landau and Gamow. The two young men—Landau was then twenty-five, and Gamow twenty-nine—had been discussing nuclear physics when it occurred to them that they could figure out some of the nuclear events taking place in the stars. Rapidly scribbling calculations on assorted scraps of paper, they started developing a formula that was to show that no lithium could exist inside the sun (a conclusion that was confirmed many years later). Their calculations were only temporarily arrested when neither could remember the size of the sun. But they did remember that it was eight light-minutes away from the earth, and rapidly devised a contraption consisting of a perforated screen facing the sun, at a certain distance from another flat screen. From the sun's image, projected through the perforation, they rapidly figured out the sun's dimensions with sufficient approximation to go on with their work. A few weeks later their conclusions were published in the British scientific journal *Nature*, under the title of "Internal Temperature of Stars." Landau and Gamow were particularly delighted with their successful scheme to publish the paper under the dateline of "Ksoochia Basa" (which they made up from the initials K.S.U.), because of Ksoochia's phonetical similarity to *sookha*, the Russian for bitch.

When they returned to Leningrad, the threat against the peaceful, intense activities of physicists in Central Europe and Russia was continuing to grow. In Göttingen and Berlin brown-shirted youth were heckling Jewish scientists, and a month after the former corporal with the funny mustache seized power, the order came that several professors at the Georgia Augusta University faculty of Natural Sciences were to be immediately retired. Many of the pundits of the new physics were Jewish, and started drifting—or being driven—away from Germany, first to Copenhagen, to England, and then chiefly to America. In the autumn of 1933, when Einstein left Berlin for the new Institute for Advanced Study in Princeton, French physicist Paul Langevin not-so-jokingly commented that "the Pope of Physics has moved and the United States will now become the center of the natural sciences."

Had the Soviets at that time taken a more amiable attitude toward foreign scientists, the tide of future world events might well have been deflected, for it was in those uneasy years, when dozens of renowned physicists were looking for a peaceful haven from Hitler's persecutions, that many of those who were to contribute to the development of atomic weapons turned to the West.

In 1932 and 1933, the Soviet Union signed nonaggression treaties with France, Poland, Finland, with the Baltic states it was later to take over, agreements with Yugoslavia, Czechoslovakia, Rumania, Iran, Turkey, and Afghanistan. In 1934 it was formally recognized by the United States, and joined the League of Nations. But this opening up was only apparent, for within the country, another man, wearing a bigger mustache, prepared to destroy those who "thrust their pig snouts into the Russian gardens," and to build around those gardens an iron fence.

Landau Lecturing: Landau holds forth in the days before his accident.

Meeting Colleagues: Here Landau enthusiastically greets visitors during a congress.

All photos from Novosty Press Agency

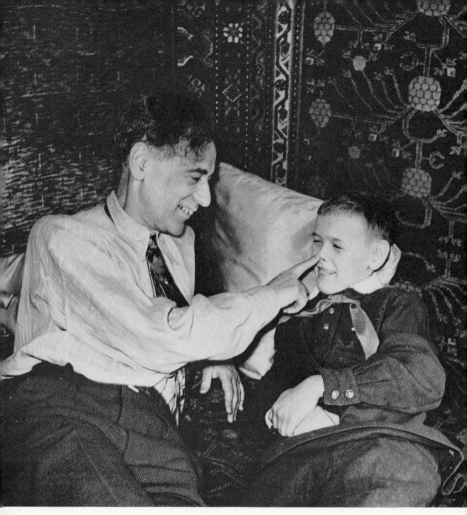

Landau and Son: Playing with his only son in a brief respite from work. This photo was taken when Igor was a schoolboy.

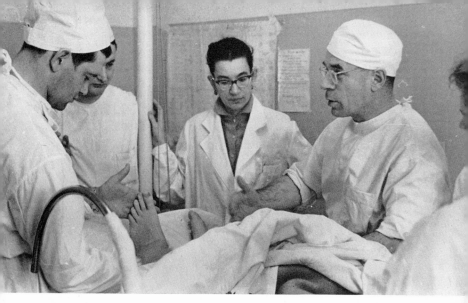

Daily Morning Round: At the right Professor Valentin Polyakoff discusses the critical situation with his colleagues.

International Brain Trust: Gathered around Landau's bedside, from left to right, are: Grashchenkov (in white cap); Garcin; Guillot; Dr. Yegorova (dark hair, facing left); an unidentified nurse and unidentified physician. Extreme right: Dr. Luchkow.

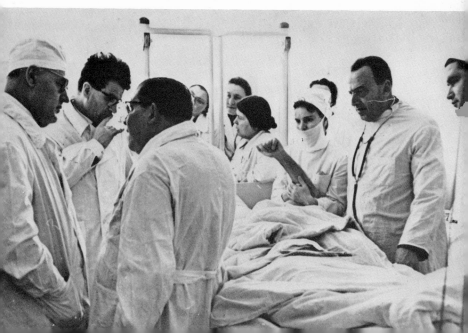

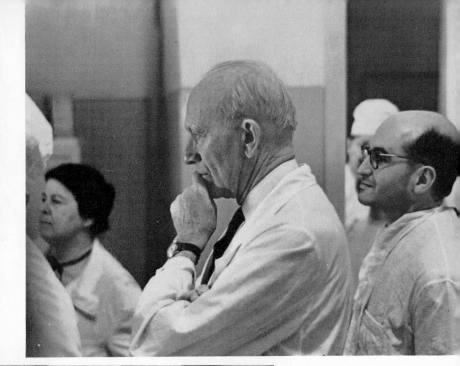

Watching and Waiting: A Russian scrub nurse peers anxiously into the operating room as a team of physicians desperately strives to save Landau's life.

Consultation: Dr. Wilder Penfield, center, listens to a report of Landau's condition with Dr. Yegorova, left, and Dr. Lifshitz, right.

Respirator: Two special Swedish respirators were brought in, one as a spare, in the event the first failed.

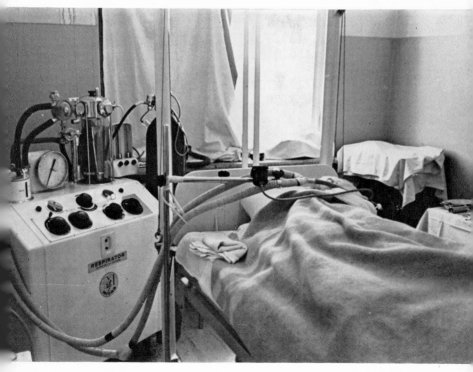

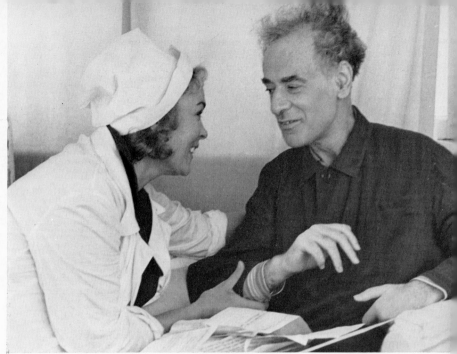

Sitting Up: At long last Landau was sufficiently recovered to sit up and talk with members of his family. First (above), his beautiful wife, Cora. Later, his son, Igor, brought him news of his colleagues. Note the clearly visible scar of the tracheotomy on Landau's neck.

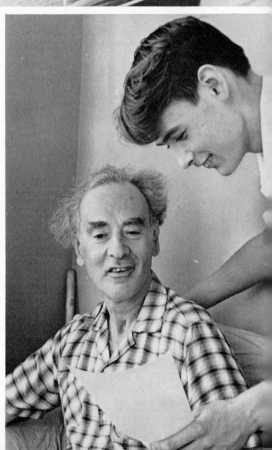

The Prize: Sweden's Ambassador to the USSR, Rolf Sohlman, at the request of the Nobel Committee, presents Landau the Nobel Prize for Physics for 1962. With his wife, Cora, standing behind him and Mstislav Keldish, president of the Soviet Academy of Sciences, looking on, Landau listens as the citation is read.

Recuperating: Landau learns how to walk again with the aid of his wife, Cora, and niece, Maya (left).

A growing suspicion of sabotage and spying was becoming endemic in the Soviet Union. The Russians, who had been eager to receive foreign scientific visitors in the past years, made no further effort to attract any. Russian scientists themselves found it increasingly difficult to go abroad. The English wife of Russian physicist Sinelnikov wrote from Kharkov to her sister in England: "You can't ask that we *both* come next year. . . . The difficulty about Kira [her husband] and me traveling together out of Russia is that the government is afraid we won't come back —so one has to stay as a sort of hostage—but I'm sure this will be remedied in time and we shall both appear on your doorstep hand in hand." (They never did.)

Piotr Kapitza, the dynamic, almost explosive physicist who had left Russia in 1921 to join Rutherford in Cambridge, had been vacationing in Russia every summer. But in the summer of 1934, after he received a professorship at Cambridge and returned to the Soviet Union once more, he found that he could no longer leave. He was appointed a member of the Academy of Sciences of the U.S.S.R., which had just moved from Leningrad to Moscow, and was told that the Soviet Union could no longer do without his services. When Rutherford wrote Russian authorities requesting that Kapitza be allowed to come back to England for the interest of science, the reply came that "Of course England would like to have Kapitza; we, for our part, would equally like to have Rutherford in the Soviet Union."

Later Kapitza was given his own institute in Moscow— in which Landau was to be the head of the theoretical physics department. The equipment from Kapitza's Cambridge laboratory, that had been built according to his specifications, was packed and shipped to Russia. "Kapitza seems very changed," wrote Sinelnikov's wife, who did not know that the scientist was, in fact, a prisoner in his own country; "not a bit like the Kapitza of our Cambridge days, nor the man who taught me one naughty word in Russian a day when I first came here. Perhaps it is because the Government has given him such tremendous responsibility."

The uneasy way of life of Soviet physicists was becoming known to their colleagues abroad, and only very few Central European scientists tried to seek haven in the Soviet Union. One of them was Austrian Fritz Houtermans, co-author of the theory of thermonuclear reactions in the sun and one of the early precursors of the utilization of atomic energy. Eventually he and others who had emigrated to the Soviet Union fell victims to assorted purges. Houtermans was imprisoned, tortured, and finally confessed to the usual charges of espionage and sabotage. In his mock confession, he had the idea of describing a "spying apparatus" of his invention, of which he even drew blueprints, hoping they would come for evaluation before Kapitza who would immediately recognize their absurdity and realize Houtermans' plight. Indeed Houtermans was "forgiven" and offered Soviet citizenship, which he evidently refused. In 1940 he was handed over to the Germans, from whom he had escaped in the first place. Several physicists suffered similar treatment in the hands of the Soviet, and it is surprising that after the war, such scientists as Houtermans were even alive.

In Leningrad, still the center of Soviet science, the long-gathering clouds burst in 1934 when Sergei Kirov, the popular (too popular, perhaps) and dynamic chairman of the Leningrad Soviet, was assassinated by a young Komsomol. The murder, which was never cleared up completely and may well have been engineered by Stalin himself, was promptly attributed to Trotskyists, widening the circle of terror and arrests led by the O.G.P.U. It was then that Landau's colleague and friend "Abatik" Bronstein was arrested. He was never to be seen at the university again, and it was learned later that he had been executed.

Eventually Stalin succeeded in liquidating Kamenev and Zinoviev, with whom he had first shared power, and now that the O.G.P.U. had served its purpose and was growing too powerful, its turn had come to be liquidated. O.G.P.U. chief Yagoda ended up in his own cells and was shot together with a large part of his staff. The O.G.P.U. was replaced by the N.K.V.D.—no lesser evil. And because many of the Bolshevik leaders that had been eliminated were Jewish, Stalin found it useful to emphasize in the newspapers and in speeches the originally Jewish names of the "traitors." Landau, who had hoped that the new order would bring an end to racial discrimination, saw a wave of anti-Semitism sweep the country.

Gamow, who had tried to be a neutralist of sorts, siding neither for nor against communism but seeking only to work in peace and enjoy life, now attempted to escape across the Afghan border, ran into a border patrol, and explained that he was only a mountain climber. He married, tried to escape again with his wife, this time by crossing the Black Sea in a sailboat. He was caught in a storm and rescued by the Soviet coast guard. Had there not been so much propaganda to encourage participation of the masses in sports and physical culture, he probably wouldn't have gotten away with the explanation that he was merely a sports enthusiast. Later Gamow, together with his wife and with the help of Madame Curie and the editor of a French communist newspaper, managed once more to be assigned to a trip aborad. He never returned to the Soviet Union, where he is considered not only as a traitor but as a bigamist. His defection no doubt contributed to closing the frontiers to further "scientific exchanges."

Dmitri Ivanienko was sent to prison and concentration camp, but eventually sailed a different course. Hand in hand with the regime, he traveled throughout the Soviet Union, giving his support to the physics of dialectical materialism. This led him to a professorship at Moscow University, which he holds to this day.

Hard-working Lev Landau, trying to steer clear of political involvements, was assigned to head the Theoretical Physics Department at the Physics-Technical Institute of the Ukrainian Academy of Sciences in Kharkov. In 1934, he had received the degree of "doctor of physical and mathematical sciences" without having to defend a thesis at Leningrad University, and in 1935, at twenty-seven, he was given the title of professor.

A city of mixed population (40 percent Russian, 40 percent Ukrainian, and 20 percent Jewish) Kharkov was a pot-pourri of old stone houses, wooden *isbas,* and new apartment buildings rising along the first, modern paved roads. Landau lived in a block of flats provided for scientific workers. (The flats are particularly well remembered by the population of Kharkov for their balconies facing Chaikovsky Street; it is from the iron bars of these balconies that the invading German armies during World War II hanged many people when they captured the city, wantonly burning or blasting two-thirds of its buildings before giving way to the counterattacking Red Army.)

It is in Kharkov that Landau founded his now famous school for young theoretical physicists, a school which grew far beyond Kharkov itself, spanning the vastness of the Soviet Union from the Baltic to the Caspian and to the remotest Siberian Far East. In a small room that served as his office (a sign on the door warned visitors: WATCH OUT—THE DIRECTOR OF THE THEORETICAL DEPARTMENT BITES), Dau was always accessible to any youngster who wanted, or believed he wanted, to become a physicist.

It was in Kharkov that Dau met Concordia Terentievna, a chemistry student whose classical Ukrainian beauty was softened by a shy smile and huge eyes that seemed to marvel when they set upon this lanky, otherworldly man whose mind seldom seemed to descend from spheres inhabited by formulas and symbols she did not understand.

Dau found in Cora a warmth he had seldom encountered in his lone-wolf life. He had many devoted friends, but aside from a few brief encounters with the opposite sex, had little experience with love. To Cora, Landau became "Dauchka"—little Dau, an affectionate diminutive of a diminutive such as Russians are fond of using. In Cora's eyes Dau was not only a famous physicist whose opinions were respected the world over, but a young dreamer who was in fact highly impractical, who looked as though he should be fed, and whose socks needed to be darned.

Dau's new girl friend couldn't but resign herself to the knowledge that science came first, and she well knew that science was a mistress who would never let a wife fully share this man's life. But she wanted to share whatever she could share.

Dau and Cora went together for many months, then were officially married. "How could you resist it," she remembers, "when the head of the Theoretical Physics Department, a respected man, knocks at your door late on a rainy night, stands in front of you, his clothes glued to his long bony frame, his hair dripping down his face, holding in his hand a soggy bouquet of flowers, and haltingly tries to ask you whether you would be his wife?" For Dau himself, whose "Theoretical-Physics approach to life" described love as a passing phenomenon, an attraction that should be enjoyed but destined to give way to boredom, this was to be, as he often called it, "an exceptionally long love."

Thus in 1937, when Piotr Kapitza asked Landau to head the theoretical section at his Moscow Institute for Physical Problems, the twenty-nine-year old Dau was no longer alone to board the train for another long journey. And for the first time in his life, his suitcase was neatly packed.

The assignment to the Moscow Institute was the best Dau could have hoped for. Moscow had replaced Leningrad as the center of Soviet science. And since his return from Copenhagen, the iron curtain had become for Landau an almost tangible reality. His colleagues abroad, who first sent him frequent invitations to attend quantum or nuclear physics gatherings or to visit their institutes in Germany, Denmark, or England, had become accustomed to receiving the same brief, embarrassed replies: "Sorry, earlier commitments prevent me from attending. . . ." "I regret, my work does not allow me . . ." Dau was a prisoner in his own country, the country to which he had returned because he wanted to serve it.

When he moved to Moscow, Landau's renown as a physicist was world-wide. He had published a dozen significant papers—not an achievement perhaps insofar as the quantity goes, but an achievement in quality, for he avoided publishing any work which he did not consider as significant, any "trivia" which might be true in itself but which did nothing to further man's knowledge of nature. A bright future seemed to smile on the young physicist.

No one in the Soviet Union, however, could count on a bright future in the late thirties, but only hope that there would be a future at all. Arrests were so unbelievably frequent that they were crippling the country, and no walk of life was spared. There was no need to prove anybody guilty beyond any reasonable doubt, before convicting him; the motto of the leaders might have been, instead, "When in doubt, arrest!" Eight army chiefs, perhaps more loyal to their country than to its dictator, were executed for "habitual betrayal of military secrets to a hostile Fascist power." The intelligentsia seemed to be a favorite target during this new wave of arrests. Even Professor Abraham Yoffe, who had acted as a director and organizer of science in the Soviet Union, who had contributed to building up research and teaching staffs of thousands in new institutes at Kharkov, Sverdlovsk, Dniepropetrovsk, Tiflis, Tomsk, Samarkand and other out-of-the-way cities, and had been richly rewarded, was worried. "I often feel as if I were living on a volcano that might erupt any time," he once commented to a foreign colleague.

Landau, who had escaped serious trouble so far, flirted with it dangerously. His outspokenness did not stop short of politics whenever the subject came up and his dander was up. His students were in constant fear that "the wrong person" might overhear his criticisms and they begged him to hold his sharp tongue. Also, in Kharkov, Landau had surrounded himself with a group of physicists many of whom happened to be Jewish. Professor Leon Rosenfeld, who accompanied Niels Bohr on a tour of the Soviet Union in 1934, remembers that it was "as if Landau had formed a Jewish clique around him." Of course the clique hadn't been planned as such, but even Landau himself, fearing a new wave of anti-Semitism, realized that it might be interpreted differently.

In Moscow Dau was somewhat safer. His friend Kapitza, who had become one of the Soviet Union's most respected physicists, had taken him under his protective wing. But safety can only be relative when day after day people around you disappear for no reason you, nor they, can understand, when a jealous colleague can dispose of you simply by reporting your involvement in subversive activities that exist only in his imagination.

That geneticist Nikolai Vavilov had been jailed and perished was at least understandable, for his genetics were too obviously deviationist. But why were such apparently harmless people as Moscow physicist Yuli Borissovich Rumer, also arrested?

It would not be surprising if Landau, in his moments of leisure, had developed his own equations and formulas to calculate the probability rates for him to be arrested, deported, or shot. If he did, there is no doubt that his equations showed that the cards were stacked against him. Nor should it be surprising that once more Dau was right.

Early in the morning one day in the winter of 1938 a black Zim limousine, Soviet Union's "official" car, drove into the courtyard of the Institute for Physical Problems on Vorobiovskaya Chaussée. A man wearing civilian clothes knocked at the door of No. 2 in one of the apartment buildings that surround the institute.

"Is Lev Davidovich Landau at home?" asked the man, when Cora opened the door. Dau slowly came down the narrow flight of stairs from his bedroom, where he liked to work and read, either stretched on his bed or sitting at his desk in front of the window facing the institute's court-yard. "Would you please come along?" the man said. "We'll explain later."

Landau dressed, put on a scarf, coat, and squared his *shapka* on his head. Fear must have been the only emo-tion in his mind, for he had always abhorred physical violence, and was afraid of the slightest pain. He kissed Cora good-bye and almost automatically told her not to worry. She stood in the doorway, frozen, watching part of her life taken away from her.

It was still dark outside and the cold grasped Landau away from the safety of home. Without a word he fol-lowed the man who courteously opened the door of the limousine and let the scientist in. "Let's go," the man told the well-trained driver who didn't even turn around to look at his new passenger. The destination was one of Moscow's most notorious political prisons, the Butyrs-kaya. Since then it has been demolished, but in those days, there were actually more prisons in the Soviet capi-tal than there were hotels.

"Follow me." Landau was led through corridors, along which passed people who did not look up, and into a small room occupied by two guards and a man in civilian clothes. The latter, sitting at a desk covered with docu-ments, asked, "Lev Landau? Lev *Davidovich* Landau?" Dau nodded. "Charges against you have been examined by the Soviet State Security Commission. You have been found guilty and sentenced to ten years in jail. You are lucky not to get the special." ("The special" was the jargon for a hard-labor camp in Siberia.)

"Guilty? Of what?" stammered Landau.

"You ought to know! You have been spying for the Germans."

CHAPTER 5

Let Knowledge Grow

(1939–1958)

IN AUGUST 1939 the Soviet people, conditioned to hate and fear Nazi Germany, learned that a nonaggression pact had been signed between it and the Soviet Union. On September 1 Hitler ordered the invasion of Poland and the Red Army marched in to close the vise, with the announcement that the Eastern territories of its uneasy Polish neighbor were being "liberated." Estonia, Latvia, and Lithuania were rapidly overrun. The Finns, who stubbornly refused to grant the territorial concessions demanded by Stalin, fought bravely.

In Moscow, perplexing news was seeping into prison cells where thousands of men, most of whom did not know why they had been arrested, waited to find out what their own fate would be. Many of the people who had been jailed were not tortured, deported to a Siberian "special," or executed. They only waited. Month after month, year after year, all but forgotten, they filled countless prisons. Nobody, it seemed, quite knew what to do with them.

Landau was among these. When World War II broke out, he had already been in jail for almost a year. He shared a cell with some forty prisoners generally termed "political," who were not required to work and were left pretty much on their own. They were allowed an occasional visit from relatives, an occasional book, or the worn-out copy of an outdated *Pravda*. Now and then a name was called out, and sometimes the man did not return; but usually, there was a new recruit to take his place.

Food was scarce, but then food had never been of much importance to Landau, who used to become so deeply immersed in work that he frequently forgot to eat, leaving untouched the snacks Cora brought him. Physically, the most cruel aspect of prison life was probably the cold. Born and raised in subtropical Baku, Landau had never become accustomed to cold, and his body's fat content was so minimal that it provided no protection and gave him only a small reserve of energy. In Moscow, where summer can be unpleasantly hot, it was only when others around him sweltered that Dau would take off his jacket and blissfully remark that at long last, a pleasantly cool summer had arrived.

Prison was unheated and damp. Winter was nearing, and most of the time Landau lay on his bunk after carefully bundling himself up in the warm clothes he had received from home, staring at the wall which had become an imaginary blackboard.

In one respect, prison even served a useful purpose, Landau later told some of his students, half seriously: in prison he learned to work without chalk, pencil, or paper, to solve the most intricate problems and equations entirely in his mind.

In prison also Landau understood for the first time the full measure of Stalin's frightening power over not only the bodies but the the minds of his subjects. During conversations with his cellmates, Dau was not surprised to find many prisoners who, like himself, had no real idea of why they were in jail. But he was amazed to discover that some had so blind a faith in Stalin that they went on praising him: they believed that someone else had engineered their arrest, unknown to the "little father." Some were even ready to grant that there might be, "in the end of ends," a good reason for them to be in jail—a reason they could not fathom but which Stalin, in his great wisdom and omniscience, had foreseen. Landau had long despised "the man who corrupted the ideal of the Revolution," and now he grew to hate him with passion. (Professor Rosenfeld remembers that when he visited the Soviet Union after Stalin's death but before the personality cult was officially denounced, Dau commented during a long conversation, "Why, when Stalin died, I danced!")

Meanwhile, Landau's friend and "boss," Piotr Kapitza, was playing an increasingly important role as chief scientific advisor to the Soviet government, and was already laying the ground for the eventual evacuation and reorganization of the physics institutes and laboratories from the western part of the country that might be threatened by war, to more remote and better protected regions, to Kazakhstan, Chelyabinsk, and Sverdlovsk, to the Urals and the Altai Mountains, to the Far East.

When Kapitza returned to Moscow and gained permission to see Landau almost a year after his arrest, he could barely recognize his friend. Always a lean person, Landau was now frighteningly emaciated. His skin was deeply drawn into the hollows of his angular, unshaven face. His hair was streaked with gray and his deep-set eyes burned with fever. When Kapitza kissed him and held him in his arms, he could feel, underneath the baggy, dirty clothes, bones that he was afraid would break.

For a long moment the two men stood speechless, un-ashamed tears rolling down their faces. Dau had a hollow cough and when he spoke his voice sounded remote, al-most unearthly, and his long thin hands were shaking in Kapitza's grip. Dau told of his arrest, of his senseless con-demnation as a German spy, of the long days and the long nights in the cold cell, and of the people who shared it with him. "I am afraid, Piotr, my friend. I am afraid I cannot stand it much longer."

When Kapitza left the prison his face was pale with anger and his fists whitened at the knuckles. To this day, Kapitza's friends at Cambridge still speak of him as a force of nature. Then, Kapitza's frustration and rage were ready to explode.

He drove to the Kremlin, identified himself, and asked to see Molotov. The Kremlin guards probably didn't quite know what to make of this angry man, who was too im-portant and too sure of himself to be shooed away. He was searched for weapons and made his way across the courtyard to the government building under the eyes of sentries behind loaded machine guns. Such were Kapitza's reputation and responsibilities that he was rapidly re-ceived by Stalin's underlings. With rare courage, at the risk of his own life, Kapitza presented them with an ultimatum: either Landau would be immediately released from jail and cleared of the senseless charge against him, or he, Kapitza, would leave the Institute of Physical Problems and refuse to work.

How close Kapitza himself came to being arrested, how Stalin may have raged when his supreme authority was challenged, will probably never be known. But Landau was released and driven to his small two-storied apartment on the institute's grounds, where Cora had waited, not knowing whether she would ever see her husband alive again.

"How fortunate I have been," Landau commented later on the rare occasions when he mentioned his arrest. "I do not think I would have survived another half-year." Without Kapitza's intervention, it is doubtful that Landau would have been released so rapidly. Physicist Yuli Borissovich Rumer, who had coauthored with Landau a whimsical book about relativity, had been arrested at the same time. He was fortunate to have a strong constitution, which enabled him to survive twenty years in jail, and he was freed only when Khrushchev denounced the personality cult of his one-time boss and launched a massive de-Stalinization campaign that was carried out with amazing efficiency. Even in the Lenin and Revolution museums near the Red Square, Stalin today has all but disappeared, as if by a miracle, from the history of the Soviet Revolution. In photographs in which he was shown next to Lenin or addressing Bolshevik meetings, his face has been replaced by other faces; his marble busts have vanished, and only on a few heroic paintings, irreplaceable masterpieces of the people's revolutionary art, can his face be identified somewhere in the background.

(It was only after this well-organized, almost Pavlovian

deconditioning process, when countless people who had met in jails went free and saw one another in the streets, that it became admissible to mention the fact that wanton arrests had been made by the thousands. "To sit" became a colloquial euphemism, "in jail" being understood but not spoken. Having spent some time in jail even became a sort of badge of honor. Russians being prolific inventors of political jokes, it wasn't long before the story started going around that job applicants were given a questionnaire in which one of the items read: "Did you 'sit' under Stalin? If you did *not*, please explain why not.")

Shortly after his release, Landau completed a study on the polarization of scattered electrons, closing a year's gap in the long list of his scientific publications. Several other theoretical analyses followed in rapid succession, the result, perhaps, of a year of thoughtful isolation.

Landau also fervently took up the interrupted teaching activities that were to be his greatest contribution to his country. Already in Kharkov young Professor Landau, head of the Theoretical Department at the Physics Institute since 1933, and of the Physics Department at Kharkov University since 1935, had developed his "theorminimum," a program for youngsters who wanted to become theoretical physicists, and had formed a group of students who became part of the backbone of Soviet science. This first crop included physicists Yevgheni Lifshitz, A. S. Kompaneietz, A. I. Akhiezer, I. Ia. Pomeranchuk, and V. C. Levich, who were now teaching in universities and institutes throughout the Soviet Union. Lifshitz, one of Dau's closest friends, had been assigned to work with him at Kapitza's Institute for Physical Problems.

In Moscow, Landau made it known that he was accessible to any youngster who wanted to become his student. His fame spread through the country. Applications and letters of recommendation came from universities in the Ukraine, Tbilisi, Erevan, Alma-Ata, from Vladivostok in Eastern Siberia. If a candidate was promising enough, he was sent to Moscow—whether he was a graduate student, or an undergraduate with no diploma at all. Landau, who refused to have a regular office at the institute, received him in a tiny room on the second floor of his apartment, scribbled down a few problems, and left him to stew.

From time to time, when he remembered about it, Landau dropped back to see how the youngster was doing. If the ordeal went on for several hours, Cora, reproaching her husband for torturing the poor boys, brought them sandwiches and a glass of milk. If the solution was too long in coming, Landau might drop a few hints. If the student was altogether too slow or seemed to be hopelessly off the track, Dau would gently send him off with the recommendation to "study up a bit more" and to come back later.

When the applicant solved and analyzed the problems to Landau's satisfaction, he was asked to return for another test, and yet another, until he reached the "Landau minimum" level. The students who passed it remember the minimum as rather high, designed not for the average good students, but to sift from the mass of physicists-to-be those who were most exceptionally gifted. (This was strikingly illustrated once when Landau was asked to supervise the final examination in a technical institute: he flunked all of the students but one. The test had to be given again by a less demanding pedagog.)

Alexei Abrikossov, who went through the mill to become Landau's favorite student in Moscow, remembers that once a candidate had met "the minimum," "Landau threw you in the water to see whether you'd swim." The candidate might now be entitled to the honor of being "Landau's student," but he wasn't even assigned a project to work on: he had to find his own. "And he'd better make sure not only that his idea was original, but that it was valid, coherent, and complete enough for Landau to accept it." Landau would not accept a project if he did not see right away that it could lead to fruitful results. Moreover, he wanted everything explained to him *his* way. To convey an idea to Landau could be a painful process, says Abrikossov. It could go on week after week, during which Landau might talk to his new disciple every day, lose his temper and leave, slamming the door or throwing up his arms, swearing that "I'll never talk to this dunce again!" or wondering, "Is this man a physicist, or a *sopojnik?*" (*Sopojnik* is the Russian for shoemaker; when someone who is not a *sopojnik* is said to work like one, the implication is definitely derogatory.) At first, many of the students who did not know Landau well enough were frightened out of their wits, until Dau returned a few days later, repenting for having been nasty and gently encouraging them in their work.

Occasionally Dau had sudden qualms about driving his team too hard. Then he would amble through the institute, awkwardly knocking things off desks or stumbling in doorways in his usual fashion, interrupting his students' work trying to make them feel at ease, talking about anything that went through his head, asking them about their girl friends, about painting or about the latest movie. When he had no newsworthy subject to bring up he would start voicing some of his already well-known opinions about literature, sports, girls, love, or beards (needless to say, none of his students wore any.) "Ah, Dau is going to spin one of his records," whispered the students, as their professor started lecturing them about ways and means of finding themselves a girl friend (a subject about which Landau had somehow acquired the reputation of being an expert).

"First of all, never talk physics to a girl," he'd say. "It will no doubt bore her terribly, and you'll get nowhere. If she understands, even worse, it will destroy her romantic and mystic notions about physicists. Find a simple girl with simple tastes; take a waitress, for instance, a blonde waitress preferably. . . . Waitresses are lovely girls, easy to get along with. Talk to her about things *she* is interested in; you can certainly find something she is interested in."

By the time his students learned Landau's approach to physics, they came to know also all of his "records" (which were later compiled in a bound volume, with illustrations.) Once a student's research project had "reached" Dau, everything usually went smoothly. He contributed new approaches, fresh ideas, helping to give the project its final shape. Triviality was trimmed off— even if this triviality was in itself correct: Landau felt that his students' work, like his own, should have the aim of eventual disclosure of some truth of nature.

Sometimes Landau himself assigned work to his older students. He seldom read scientific publications, only scanning them to spot here and there something that might be of interest. He then handed the paper to one of the young physicists, asking him to figure it out, and to present the work during a seminar. He seldom wrote, either. He explained his ideas to his students, enlisting the assistance of one or the other to write a coherent paper for publication, if he felt the work was worth publishing.

Once new students became accustomed to Landau's temper and personality, they realized that they did not have to go out of their way to please or to pacify him. Now they were accepted, beardless as they were, as "one of Dau's boys," which implied a certain status. There were no "Dau's girls" at the institute; though Landau did not deny that women might have enough brains to become physicists, he avoided having any female students. "If I had as many worries as a woman, I would never have become a physicist," he noted.

Underlying his roughness, students discovered a genuine kindness, a desire to please and to be useful, a sense of humor that manifested itself daily, even in his work. A theoretical approach was taken to examine any problem that might come up; fantastic formulae were developed to explain human emotions or world events. Once Dau and a group of students set out to organize an "International Congress of Pathological Physics." The president of the congress was to be a famous British astrophysicist, now dead. Some of the chief participants were selected among Soviet scientists, notably from Moscow University; many Japanese physicists were included "because of their ability to unveil a great deal of triviality." Scientific papers published in the world's literature were mercilessly dissected to the bone, which sometimes wasn't there. "Now, this is very definitely pathology and should be presented at the congress," Dau would comment in such cases. "Without the bone, it does not stand up."

Dr. Kurt Mendelssohn, reader in Physics at Oxford University, wrote after a trip to the Soviet Union: "Coupling his acute and devastating criticism with great human kindliness, Landau, who by many scientists on both sides of the Curtain is considered the most outstanding theoretical physicist of our time, has created a large school of

gifted and devoted pupils which has not its equal anywhere in the world."

There is no doubt that Landau's contribution to the development of physics in the Soviet Union was greater than
anybody else's. After the war, when many of the "International Set of Physics" had moved from Central Europe
to the United States, Landau helped bring Soviet physics
to an amazingly high level, and he was in great part re-
sponsible for the shocked surprise in the United States
when Russia took the lead, if only briefly, in the development of the hydrogen bomb.

Dau was particularly proud of his school, and carefully
followed up everyone who had passed through his examination room—alternately known as the torture chamber.
He kept a long, untidy list, which no one but himself
could decipher. Each name was followed by assorted
comments, checkmarks, circles, asterisks or exclamation
marks, dates showing when tests were given, question
marks indicating that even when a student flunked, Dau
wondered whether he would return. Some names were
crossed off, sometimes with a brief remark: "Hopeless" . . .
"Not a physicist."

On the list a patient reader might find the names of
students who have now taken their place among the leading young physicists in the Soviet Union: Professor Alexei
Abrikossov, "Aliosha," who remained at the Institute for
Physical Problems, together with A. B. Migdal and I. M.
Khalatnikov (known as "Khalat," the Russian for dressing
gown.) V. B. Berestetski, Ia. A. Smorodinsky, I. S.
Shmushkevich, K. A. Ter-Martirossian, and many others,
now researchers or professors throughout the Soviet
Union, representing several "generations" of physicists
and theoreticians.

The staff and students of the Institute for Physical

Problems met at least twice a week for seminars that were so informal they were described by a visiting American as "rather like scientific bull sessions." On Wednesdays there was the seminar run by Piotr Kapitza, not unlike the former Kapitza Club, the weekly gathering of "young Turks" at Cambridge in the nineteen-twenties. In 1945 Kapitza was fifty-one years old, still possessing apparently inexhaustible sources of energy that enabled him to be carried away with experiments right on through the night, and to have enough left in the morning to describe, with unmitigated delight, his most spectacular results to his students.

And on Thursday mornings, there was the theoretical seminar run by Landau. Exactly at 11 A.M. "Promptness is the courtesy of kings," Landau used to say, adding, on the rare occasions when one of his students turned up late, "Ah, I'm afraid you'll never be a king, young man."

Landau did not preside from the rostrum nor pontificate from a desk, but usually sat with the audience, in the front row. A student would go up to the blackboard, to make a report or start a discussion, and a casual visitor might have wondered, at first, who was running the show. Then, an unexpected, probing, precise question would come from the tall, ascetic figure with a crop of slightly graying dark hair. Sometimes Landau impatiently jumped up, took a piece of chalk and started scribbling on the blackboard, mixing esoteric scientific comments with such interjections as "nonsense," "pathology," or "trivia! pure trivia."

If Landau asked one of his students to work on a report and the work was sloppily prepared, the man would be violently reprimanded. And if this was repeated, he would lose face; Dau would give him up, until the student found a way to redeem himself. If a report was good, a heated discussion could usually be expected that would go on far past lunchtime, frequently to culminate in the solution of the problem at hand, and often concluded by somebody's remark from the back row that, "Of course, Dau was right again!"

Subjects covered a wide range. Landau fought the modern trend toward specialization in a narrow field of physics, remaining one of the world's few theoretical physicists familiar with all of its aspects. "I have many interests and I am probably one of the few remaining universalists in physics," Landau once told Danil Semenovich Danin, one of the Soviet Union's top science writers. "Don't take this as boasting," he added. "Simply, when I started in physics, all theoreticians were universalists, dealing with any problem. Few have kept this style, and universalism went sour because theoretical physics has grown so much."

Kapitza once wrote:

Landau's clarity of thought and precise style of work have helped him bring up several generations of physicists. . . . He is one of the few physicists to whom you may address a question on anything in this field, and receive a truly thorough answer. Landau's theoretical method has an important feature: he does not separate theory from experiment. This is what he teaches the young ones.

Another physicist, Landau's old friend Rudolph Peierls, now Professor of Theoretical Physics at Oxford University, wrote:

To any problem which he tackles, whether it be in the quantum theory of fields, theory of solids or liquids, or any other topic, he will bring the same outlook, the same insistence on recognizing the basic and simple features of the situation, the same recognition of analogies with known situations and finally, the formulation of a mathematical description appropriate to the particular purpose.

For him mathematics is always a tool which may have to take sophisticated forms when required, but whose intricacies should never detract from the main purpose of understanding the basic ideas. He can be very impatient of excessive mathematical rigour, and readers of his papers are expected to follow his intuitive judgement on points not worthy of elaborate mathematical proof.

Even to the noninitiated, the list of areas to which Landau made significant contributions gives an idea of his "universalism": Properties of metals at very low temperature, dispersal of light by light, sources of stellar energy, loss of sound in hard bodies, superconductivity, quantum field theory, diamagnetism, phase transformation of solids, superfluidity of liquid helium, and many others, treating specialized areas, a single one of which might be enough to occupy a scientist with less breadth, in which Landau's formulations are now considered as classical.

Dau liked to work in the prone position, on his bed; if he didn't need to use a pencil and paper, he comfortably clasped his hands behind his head. As is almost traditional with physicists, an idea and the urge to develop it could come at any time and at any place. (One of his students claims that this occurred one day when Dau, completely rehabilitated after his release from prison, was invited to a reception at the Kremlin. The reception was televised and on the screen, behind Khrushchev, who was making a short speech, the students saw Landau. Dau, it seems, was trying to get away from the camera and was frantically searching for a piece of paper on which he wanted to jot down "something physical" that had just occurred to him.)

Landau seldom bothered to write down detailed results; once he was satisfied he was on the right track, he might take a few notes and reserved the elaboration of the idea for one of his Thursday seminars. Frequently a question was sufficient to trigger a new theory. A typical example of Dau's creative process is remembered by physicist Artem Alichanian, director of the Institute of Physics of the Armenian Academy of Sciences, and head of a cosmic radiation station some nine thousand feet up the Aragatz Mountain. For several months, Alichanian had been searching for a formula to express some of the ionization processes of cosmic particles, and during a visit to Moscow, he dropped in to see Landau. During the conversation, Alichanian asked Landau whether he had any ideas on the matter. Stretched on his bed, his long feet spread in a V, Landau listened carefully, and a few minutes later jotted down a few figures and started talking to his Armenian colleague. Soon he had developed a completely new theoretical explanation of an aspect of cosmic radiation—now known as one of the many "Landau equations."

In 1945, Landau could view his life with some satisfaction. At thirty-seven, he was the Soviet Union's top theoretical physicist. He could work pretty much as he pleased, surrounded by a group of devoted students and close friends. The Landaus lived comfortably, having a whole apartment at their disposal, with their own kitchen and bathroom. They had a one-year-old son, Igor, and Igor too had his own room. They had no material preoccupations; scientists in the Soviet Union had emerged in the upper layer of the classless society, and salaries were high. Landau was not particularly concerned with money, and Cora ran the household. She had arranged for them to buy a country *dacha*, which probably didn't even cost as much as the 200,000 or so rubles that came with the Stalin and Lenin prizes Dau had received. (This was 200,000 rubles in the old currency, roughly equivalent to $2,000. The government allowed private citizens to build small country houses on plots allotted to them, and in principle the cost of the building was to be reimbursed by the state, and the house would become government property. In fact, most of the *dachas* remained private, and could be sold by the owner, sometimes for rather stiff prices. A few have been known to sell for as much as 30,000 or 40,000 new rubles, over $40,000 in the current exchange rate.)

Since he had spent a year in jail, Landau had learned to be more subdued in the expression of his political opinions, but still remained somewhat suspect. The artificial gap between Marxists and "bourgeois" physics was as wide as ever, and Landau was dangerously close to the latter. For more than ten years now he had not been allowed to leave the country, and saw no immediate hope of visiting his former friends and colleagues in Denmark or England, not to speak of America (many of the German and Central European physicists who had emigrated to the United States had stayed there).

Politically unreliable, Landau had never been a member of the Party, nor had he been elected to the Soviet Academy of Sciences, the country's highest scientific body. Membership in the Academy depended on both the scientific achievements and the political texture of a candidate. Whenever an election was held to fill a vacancy, a list of preferred candidates was prepared by the Central

Committee of the Communist Party, a list which included no "pink" scientists, only truly red ones. The list did not completely limit the choice of the electing membership, but merely "recommended" that, in doubtful cases, when candidates had equal scientific merits, the ones selected by the Central Committee should be given preference. But as the membership of the Academy included a large majority of party members, many of whom had themselves been on the "preferred list," the election of non-party candidates was rare, particularly under Stalin. Landau, one of the exceptions, was finally elected only in 1945, chiefly because he received the support of physicists who either threatened to leave the Academy or refused to become members, until Landau himself was appointed. Mikhail Leontovich and Igor Tamm, two of the Soviet Union's top physicists (the latter later received the Nobel Prize) gave Landau particularly strong support. After their plea, even though Landau was conspicuous by his absence from the Central Committee list, he was unanimously elected to full membership in the Academy, bypassing the intermediary stage of corresponding member.

Political interference was still frequent in physics, and Landau took (and expected his students to follow) a strong stand against people whose actions he found dishonest. Landau's moral standards in such cases can be summed up simply: It was wrong, he used to say, to engage in "active evil," which consisted of purposefully seeking to cause harm. Thus one Muscovite physicist, Professor Y., was completely ostracized by Landau and "his boys" because he had been actively evil. Professor Y. had written a paper, brimming with ideological undertones, to criticize the work of a young theoretician whose political position was already precarious. When Professor Y's criticism was published, the young man, already in semi-exile in a far-off Siberian laboratory, was threatened with dismissal (though eventually he succeeded in keeping his job, perhaps because he was the only physicist that the laboratory in question had been able to secure). Ever since, Landau had refused to associate with Y.

Landau himself frequently had been on the brink of disgrace, for his talent, his outspokenness, paired with unorthodox political views, made him a prime target for physicists who envied him, or who feared that he might threaten their own position. Former Leningrad "musketeer" Dmitri Ivanienko apparently belonged to the latter category: now a professor at Moscow University, the huge, birthday-cakelike building overlooking Moscow from Lenin's Hills, Ivanienko did his best to prevent Landau from receiving a professorship there, perhaps because Dau would have become too powerful a rival.

In 1949 Landau published a series of lectures on general physics, and, with the help of Yevgheni Lifshitz, worked on the monumental task of writing a six-volume textbook on theoretical physics. This text, treating nearly every aspect of theoretical physics, was published only after lengthy birth pains, because it did not support dialectical-materialistic views on physics. Later it was translated into several foreign languages and became a classic the world over. In the U.S.S.R., however, it was the target of many a political broadside. The most threatening attack took the form of a critical review that amounted to a denunciation of Landau and Lifshitz as deviationists. The reviewer, physicist Tereletski, charged not only that Landau and Lifshitz advocated Niels Bohr's ideas on complementarity, but that they didn't avocate them openly but in a devious, subversive way that might lead students to accept these ideas without realizing they were going against "the victorious tide of dialectical materialism."

This preposterous charge, which could only be taken seriously in the suspicion-laden atmosphere that prevailed under Stalin, could have had unpleasant consequences, for it implied that Landau and Lifshitz were trying to corrupt the younger generations of Soviet physicists. Such massive intellectual sabotage could have brought about reprisals, but the situation was unwittingly saved by Vladimir Fok, Landau's former teacher in Leningrad, now a highly respected elderly gentleman, somewhat out of touch with the trends of modern physics. Fok at that time was preparing an assault against Bohr's "positivism and idealism," and even went to Copenhagen to have a discussion with Bohr himself. Physicists in Denmark remember the discussion as particularly nebulous: Bohr, who was barely intelligible to people who weren't used to his way of speaking, pleasantly received Fok, who was himself nearly deaf. From the exchange of opinions with Bohr, Fok heard only what he wanted to hear, and Bohr had difficulty in following the ideas of his foreign guest. The meeting did not lead to complete understanding, but Fok nevertheless returned to the Soviet Union persuaded he had convinced Bohr that Bohr was wrong. Fok promptly published several articles and gave interviews to the lay press, making it apparent that physics had finally been rescued from bourgeois idealism. In the resulting enthusiasm charges against Landau were forgotten or forgiven, and the six-volume textbook, slightly revised, became widely used throughout the Soviet Union, eventually earning their authors the Lenin Prize and an award of 7,500 rubles (about $8,000).

Meanwhile Stalin, aging and grizzled, continued to

tighten his grip on the country, fueling a constant, psychotic fear of spies, saboteurs, and assassins. In January 1953 it seemed that a new era of terror and purges was being prepared when Stalin denounced the "White Blouses Plot" (or the "Doctors' Plot") in which he saw himself the victim of Jewish physicians attempting to precipitate his death. A number of doctors were jailed and Jews throughout the country arrested. Stalin literally locked himself up in his fortresslike residence on the Lenin Hills, facing the meandering Moskva River and the Novodevichi Monastery where his wife, Svetlana, was buried. He hardly left the house, completely isolated himself at night, without even any servants, surrounded by two rows of guards bristling with weapons, protected by steel doors and machine guns.

On the evening of March 5, after Stalin had given no sign of life for a day, and his telephone did not answer, the captain of the guard knocked at the door, in vain. He called the Kremlin, and Khrushchev, Beria, Bulganin and Malenkov motored to the villa. Passing the first row of guards, they dismounted and were searched for weapons. The door was broken down and they entered the silent house, calling for Stalin. Finally they walked into his bedroom and found the old dictator sprawled on the floor, his glassy eyes staring, motionless, at the ceiling. The story goes that one of the four exclaimed, "At last, the son of a bitch is dead"—when Stalin, paralyzed but conscious, seemed to come alive and fiercely rolled his eyes. The four fell on their knees, begging forgiveness. Then Stalin finally succumbed to the hemorrhage that had stricken his brain.

Such was the panic at the death of the man who had ruled the Soviet Union for three decades, so deeply conditioned was the devotion of the Soviet people to their leader, that Stalin's death was not revealed for several days, while his succession took shape. When his embalmed body* lay in state off fashionable Gorki Street dozens of men and women were trampled to death by the huge crowd that came to view it. The entire country was almost panic-stricken: the cult was still alive, but the god was dead.

"What will happen to Russia now?" a student mournfully asked Professor Landau, who had not waited for de-Stalinization to proclaim Stalin's death a happy event. "You fool," answered Dau. "Nothing worse than Stalin could ever happen to Russia. We are entering a new era."

Indeed, the liberalization later encouraged by Khrushchev gave the Soviet people more freedom than they had ever tasted before, and cracks appeared in the iron curtain. An increasing number of foreign visitors came to the Soviet Union, and Landau received in his home physicists he had met nearly thirty years earlier in Göttingen, Cambridge, or Copenhagen. His activities, particularly in the teaching of physics, redoubled; he was asked to lecture at Moscow University, toured several institutes in the Soviet Union. The ideological differences between Marxist and "bourgeois" physics became less acute, and could almost officially be viewed with some humor. Science writer Danin published a popular book on physics, in which these differences were lightly commented upon by an anonymous physicist:

"Look," said the physicist with an ironical smile when he reached the restaurant in which participants in the 1959 Inter-

---

* An aging mortician named Zbarski, who had embalmed Lenin's body so well thirty years earlier, was released from concentration camp to embalm Stalin as well.

national Physics Congress in Kiev were having a snack. "Look. There sits Heisenberg the idealist, and next to him Fok the materialist. Their disagreement does not prevent them from swallowing the fruits of nature and digesting them. But wait . . . You see, old Heisenberg is swallowing some kind of pill. Perhaps nature after all has punished him for his disbelief in its objective existence? But then, why has nature punished Fok? You see, Fok cannot hear well, he has a little microphone and hearing apparatus. . . . But they sit and have a friendly talk, in spite of their disagreement. Do you know why? Because they are talking business. Bu-si-ness!"

When Landau reached his fiftieth birthday on January 22, 1958, and drank champagne toasts only to the ladies (letting his students substitute for drinking to his male friends' health), his star was higher than ever.

He was in peak form, unusual for a physicist of that age. Berestetski, one of Landau's former students, wrote then: "Theoretical physics holds a position among the sciences that can be compared in a sense to the position of ballet in the arts and of *futbol* (soccer) in sports. Here talents usually develop early, but likewise, fade away early too. Landau is a fortunate exception to this rule. It can be said with an absolutely clear conscience that Landau meets his fiftieth year in the flower of his creative strength."

CHAPTER 6

A Thermonuclear Parenthesis: Who Made the Soviet H-Bomb?

AT THE beginning of August 1953 seismographs in Asia and in Alaska indicated that either a minor earthquake, or an explosion of considerable magnitude, had taken place somewhere in the Siberian wastes. On August 8, Malenkov, Stalin's first successor, made the announcement that the Soviet Union now possessed the hydrogen bomb, and a few days later a "flying laboratory" of the U. S. Radiation Detection Patrol collected samples of rain and tiny particles in the atmosphere over Asia. Analysis showed beyond any doubt that the Soviet Union had exploded a thermonuclear bomb, probably utilizing a light lithium core, whose fusion had been triggered by an atomic device. The explosive site was later identified as the Siberian island of Wrangel in the Arctic circle, due west of Point Barrow, Alaska.

An eventuality which Americans had generally regarded as remote had come true: the Soviet Union had taken the lead in the race for the "ultimate weapon." Everything indicated that the Russians possessed a lightweight thermonuclear device a thousand times more powerful than the atom bomb that had leveled Hiroshima. There was little doubt that the Russians were now engaged in the manufacture of hydrogen bombs, against which the United States could retaliate only with the atomic bomb, which had suddenly become a relatively feeble deterrent.

The analysis of fallout particles indicated that the Soviets had taken a completely new approach in the development of their bomb. They had apparently used a "chemical trigger," instead of relying solely on the atomic bomb to produce the tremendous heat and pressure necessary to fuse together two forms of heavy hydrogen—deuterium and tritium—that are followed by the release of thermonuclear energy. It appeared also that the Russians even boosted their explosion by introducing a third stage into their bomb, consisting of a light metal, lithium: the atomic and chemical trigger set off the deuterium and tritium, which in turn ignited the fusion of lithium.

In the United States government leaders of both parties realized the danger of the new position of their country in the armament race, but the American public was not immediately made aware of the Russian superiority. Senator Stuart Symington, Missouri Democrat, commented, "Russia may now have military and atomic superiority over the United States, which, coupled with initiative and surprise, could prove decisive in atom or hydrogen bomb war." And Representative Stirling Cole, New York Republican, noted, "The Russian bomb can be delivered by air—that's why I am so disturbed and troubled."

Much of the public held the mistaken impression that the two great rival powers were now on equal terms in the development of hydrogen weapons. This impression came from the explosion, eight months earlier, of the world's first thermonuclear device, designed by American scientists. But it was not generally known that MIKE, which exploded on November 1, 1952, wiping from the face of the earth the islet of Elugelab in the Marshall Islands, was not really a bomb. It was, rather, a 65-ton factory, which had to be shipped off piece by piece and assembled on Elugelab. It contained elaborate refrigerating machinery, necessary because the tritium needed for the explosion was an artificial hydrogen isotope that had to be kept at a constantly low temperature. By no stretch of the imagination was MIKE a military weapon, unless one envisaged, as a scientist put it, lugging it into enemy territory aboard several oxcarts, and assembling it there.

Already in 1949, the American government had been astonished by the explosion of the first Soviet atomic bomb, which was not expected until some ten or twenty years later. This was attributed in a great part to a well-organized network of "atomic spies," notably the Rosenbergs. When the Russian H-bomb was exploded, however, a similar explanation could no longer be valid. (Though President Eisenhower indicated in a press conference on October 8, 1953, that Soviet physicists had material assistance from what they learned of the United States program through espionage.)

In fact, it appears now that the story was quite different. A *New York Times* article by Harry Schwartz, reprinted in the *Bulletin of the Atomic Scientists,* noted:

It can be authoritatively stated that the Soviet advance revealed last August surprised United States technicians and touched off an all-out American effort to duplicate the Soviet feat. Most surprising was the fact that the Soviet technique used last August showed that the Russians had proceeded along quite a different line from that employed earlier by the United States and Great Britain, a line that had been communicated to the Soviet government by the convicted atom spy, Dr. Klaus Fuchs.

Fuchs, who came to Los Alamos in December 1944 as one of Rudolph Peierls' brightest students, had no access to detailed information about the United States thermonuclear device, because none was available before he returned to England. Fuchs may have been present at a special conference in Los Alamos in 1946, during which the super bomb was discussed, but notions about how to make it were still so vague that the meeting broke up in disagreement over whether the hydrogen bomb was at all feasible or not. Fuchs was arrested in England in 1950, and the last information he conveyed to the Soviets could not possibly have given them a way to develop a bomb which no one, at that time, knew how to make. (The fact that J. Robert Oppenheimer, Edward Teller, and Hans Bethe, took as far back as 1944 a patent on the development of the hydrogen bomb, in no way indicates they knew, at that time, how to manufacture it. They only pointed out the general principles along which it could work.)

The first American plans for a thermonuclear device seem to have tumbled under the criticism of Polish mathematician Stan Ulam, who suggested another idea that was developed chiefly by Teller and led to the creation of MIKE. In August 1953, when the Soviet H-bomb exploded, Teller, John von Neumann, and a group of scientists were still working on the development of a "dropable" bomb, a project referred to as "the sausage." It was

realized on March 1, 1954, six months after the explosion
of the Russian hydrogen bomb, on the atoll of Bikini. (It
was this bomb that created a storm of nuclear fallout
which drifted south—instead of north, as meteorologists
had forecast—and descended upon a Japanese steam
trawler whose fishermen suffered from severe radiation
burns and poisoning.)

Obviously there had been a gross underestimation of
the capabilities of Soviet scientists—an underestimation
which was not dissipated by the Soviet H-bomb blast
and was evidenced again in the first episodes of the space
race a few years later. By general agreement Soviet science
was considered as somewhat backward. This was a satis-
fying state of public opinion that was not actively discouraged by office holders in search of re-election. Such an
underestimation was also fostered by the Russian inclina-
tion for secrecy and, on another level, by recurrent reports
in the press of such significant facts as that the Moskvich
automobile was a copy of an early model of the Rambler,
that the latest Zim bore a resemblance to a now outdated
Cadillac, and that bathtub plugs were lacking in Russian
hotels.

Also it had long been obvious that in the Soviet Union,
modern science was at odds with Marxist ideology, and it
was understandably assumed that this conflict had arrested
the development of science at a somewhat juvenile stage.
In fact, from the first days of the Revolution, scientists in
Russia started receiving infinitely more support than they
had been given in Czarist times. Scientists had materially
good working conditions, and, being the type of persons
scientists often are, the ideological restrictions may have
only spurred the independence of their minds.

Another error was the belief that the Soviet Union did
not possess any uranium, when in fact, a thorough explor-

ation of the mineral resources of the country, which Lenin considered of paramount importance to the development of the first Socialist state, had revealed large uranium deposits that were tapped already before the war. The properties of uranium were diligently investigated and in 1940, a young, foxy-faced Russian physicist, G. N. Flerov (now at the Joint Institute for Nuclear Physics in Dubna) assisted by K. A. Petryak (at the Radium Institute in Leningrad) made the discovery of spontaneous fission of this element.

After the 1930s several institutes in the Soviet Union devoted much effort to nuclear research—among them, the Roentgen Institute and the Physics-Technical Institute in Leningrad, the S. I. Vavilov Institute of Physical Problems in Moscow, and the Physics-Technical Institute in Kharkov.

Landau had been, at one time or another, a member of each. Already in Leningrad he studied, among other things, the properties of uranium, and the thermonuclear processes in the sun, first theorized in Göttingen in 1928 by Fritz Houtermans and Geoffrey Atkinson. Landau's friend George Gamow, whose mind already reached for the stars, remembers lecturing in 1932 about Atkinson's and Houtermans' theory that the sun is fueled by the fusion of light nuclei, like the hydrogen bomb. After the lecture he was approached by Nikolai Bukharin (an early revolutionary leader executed as a right-winger during the 1938 purges) who wanted Gamow and other Leningrad scientists to try to achieve the same reaction on earth. Bukharin even offered Gamow the possibility of using, during the night, nearly all of the electric current generated in the city. Had this project been carried through, the course of history might have been considerably altered.

Two years later, during a hiking trip in the Caucasus, Landau mentioned to Rudolph Peierls that it would be sufficient, in order to obtain an almost inexhaustible source of energy, to find a way to achieve a controlled emission of neutrons in order to produce at least as many as would be used up in the process—describing, in fact, the chain reaction later realized by Joliot-Curie in France. And a few years later, the Russians built one of Europe's first cyclotrons, an atomic accelerator essential for the study of the nucleus.

Landau's former teacher, Yakov Frenkel, earlier branded as a "deviationist from Marxist science," gave in the late thirties an explanation of fission processes in uranium, and by April 1940 the Soviet Academy of Sciences had so well realized this element's potential importance that it created a Uranium Problem Commission, which listed among its members nearly all of the top physicists in the Soviet Union. (Landau was not, at first, called upon to participate in the solution of problems connected with uranium; when the commission was created by the Academy, Dau was "sitting" in a prison nearby, sufficiently preoccupied with his own problems.)

At that time uranium was discussed so openly in the Soviet Union that a few months later *Izvestia* ran an article about its possibilities as a source of unlimited energy, and Piotr Kapitza mentioned in a lecture in 1941 that, theoretically, a single atom bomb could destroy a city of several million people.

In 1941 Kapitza was in charge of the safety of equipment and personnel for all of the Soviet physics-technical institutes, and during the German invasion, he crisscrossed the country, directing the reorganization of Soviet physics in new laboratories at a safe distance from the battlefield. This was a momentous and well-prepared project: all of the machinery at the Kharkov Institute, for example, was loaded on a train overnight and shipped to Ufa, the capital of the Bashkir S.S.R. in the southwestern Urals, where the entire Ukrainian Academy of Sciences had been transferred.

During the long and bloody struggle against the German invader, much of the Soviet scientific talent was diverted toward more immediate technical projects, and it seems that the goal of producing atomic weapons was postponed, as their realization was not considered possible in terms of the immediate war effort.

But in a study of Soviet science, undertaken on behalf of the U.S. Armed Forces, the Rand Corporation reported that by 1943 the Russians had resumed their atomic development program. Kapitza was then back at the Institute for Physical Problems in Moscow, where he and Landau became members of the Soviet equivalent of the Manhattan Project, which must have involved, as it did in the United States, a large portion of the country's top physicists.

The Soviet scientists, however, were far behind their American colleagues, who had been working since 1941 in relatively peaceful conditions, with an amazing amount of equipment and personnel placed at their disposal, and with the assistance of some of the world's top physicists. Literally hundreds of scientists had been drafted into the Manhattan Project: Niels Bohr (who had escaped from Denmark), Edward Teller, Leo Szilard, Hans Bethe, Rudolph Peierls, Enrico Fermi, George Gamow are only a few among those who came from Europe and became, at one time or another, involved in the development of nuclear weapons. Physicists in Los Alamos were provided with every facility that science and technology could muster—notably the use of computing machines, necessary to carry out thousands of time-consuming calculations, machines which were lacking in the Soviet Union at the beginning of the war.

Even more than in the United States—where out of thousands involved in the Manhattan Project, only a few knew what it was all about—the nuclear weapons committee in the Soviet Union was shrouded in the strictest secrecy. To this day not a single significant detail of the Soviet teamwork has been officially revealed, and even the most logical assumptions must be made with caution.

Did Kapitza, for instance, carry on as one of the top physicists in the project, a role that he was eminently qualified for? Some reports indicate that in 1946, after experimental atom bomb tests in Bikini, Kapitza may have been tempted to join those scientists who refused to do further work in the development of nuclear weapons. Kapitza was quoted as saying, "To speak about atomic energy in terms of the atomic bomb is comparable to speaking about electricity in terms of the electric chair." This statement is believed to have prompted Stalin to dismiss Kapitza from his position as director of the Institute for Physical Problems, and it is known that Kapitza was "exiled" to his country home at Zvenigorod near Moscow, where he continued to work, under house arrest, for several years. Others report that Kapitza's disgrace had nothing to do with the atom bomb, but resulted from another incident that occurred during the war when Kapitza was called upon to help Russia produce an increasing amount of steel needed for armament. It seems that

Kapitza suggested a method for obtaining liquid air, which he had developed in Cambridge. Leading Soviet cryogenic engineers (specialists in techniques using extremely low temperatures) objected to his proposal, claiming that their method would be more efficient, but Kapitza's fame led Stalin to choose his technique. After the fall of Germany, when the Red Army occupied German factories, it turned out that the Germans themselves were using the same method that had been suggested by the Russian engineers, and that this method was more effective than the method proposed by Kapitza.

An old Cambridge friend tells that Kapitza was then summoned to a meeting with the Russian engineers to discuss the matter, but did not appear. The next day he was dismissed as director of the institute, and retired to his Zvenigorod *dacha* where he stayed until he was rehabilitated in 1952 or 1953. Hence it can be assumed that Russia's top experimental physicist did not actively participate in the development of Soviet nuclear weapons—unless he was pardoned just for that purpose.

Another story, only whispered in Russia, actually names "the father of the Soviet H-bomb", describing the incident which enabled the Russians to have their "droppable" thermonuclear device six months before the Americans did.

The incident takes place early in 1952 in the old, somewhat baroque palace full of mementoes of the Czarist past, that serves as headquarters for the Soviet Academy of Sciences in Moscow. A select committee of nuclear scientists was gathered to review progress accomplished toward the development of the hydrogen bomb. Igor Tamm presided at the meeting. Among the participants were some of the Soviet Union's top experts: Frenkel,

Landau, Flerov, Blokhintsev, Frank, Brodsky, Kurshatov, as well as Mtstislav Keldysh, a mathematician and later an astronautical specialist, the chief contributor to the development of the Soviet computer technique who made it possible to carry out the complex calculations essential to the precise determination of thermonuclear processes that would take place in a fraction of a second. (In the United States, the Los Alamos team, using the latest electronic brains such as ENIAC and MANIAC, was still faced with such a tremendous amount of mathematical computations that the computer section worked around the clock, alternating between day and night shifts.)

The Soviet scientists assembled at the Academy were reviewing the work of hundreds of physicists, mathematicians, and technicians, who were sharing (most of them, without knowing it) work leading to the development of the H-bomb. The job of the committee was to fit hundreds of individual contributions in the large picture that only a few were privileged to contemplate. As the meeting started, Igor Tamm, facing the high-level commissars who submitted to Stalin routine progress reports about the superbomb, is reported to have been somewhat embarrassed. A few days earlier one of his students, Andrei Dmitrievich Sakharov, had learned a secret he was not privy to. Sakharov had received from Tamm the usual piecemeal, anonymous assignment, and after solving it, handed it back with the brief and disturbing remark: "So, I see you're working on the thermonuclear bomb!"

Tamm first tried to deny this assumption, but the young physicist would not bite. "All right, all right." Sakharov shrugged. "If you say you're not working on the thermonuclear bomb, you're not working on the thermonuclear bomb. But if by any chance you were, I could tell you of a much better way to go about it."

When Tamm reported this incident to the gathered scientists and political commissars, there was an apparent concern that the secret had been revealed to "an outsider." "And where is this young man now?" someone asked. Tamm replied that he had told Sakharov to wait in the hall, and now summoned him to expose his idea.

As the young physicist started talking, the qualms of the H-bomb team disappeared to be replaced by intense interest. Sakharov had just outlined an entirely new line of work, that could lead to the development not of a huge and bulky thermonuclear device such as the American MIKE, but to an actual bomb, that could rapidly be manufactured. Sakharov's idea was to build a fission-fusion-fission bomb, in which the central atomic explosion and a "chemical trigger" would ignite the thermonuclear fusion of deuterium and tritium, which in turn would start off the fusion of a light metal—lithium. His proposal was strikingly simple, but so remote from the line that had been followed so far, that the committee hesitated. Tamm, who had had the time to study Sakharov's proposal in some depth, believed that an all-out effort should be made in that direction, abandoning the tritium bomb. Landau, after scribbling a few notes on his pad, agreed, while more conservative physicists (and, probably, the politically-minded party members who might have suspected sabotage) held out for the earlier approach, presumably the same that enabled United States scientists to explode their sixty-five-ton "kluge" on Elugelab.

The final decision was that two groups would work simultaneously, following both paths, and it was suggested that Tamm take charge of the Sakharov project.

"Why me?" Tamm is reported to have protested, designating, instead, the originator of the idea, the obscure thirty-two-year-old physicist who suddenly found himself at the head of a group of respected elders—including Tamm himself.

In August 1953, when the world's first droppable thermonuclear bomb was exploded on Wrangel Island, Sakharov must have sighed with relief. Two months later he was elected to full membership of the Soviet Academy of Sciences, bypassing, like Landau, the usual intermediary stage of corresponding member.

After the first American hydrogen bomb was exploded six months later, the United Press quoted a "Washington source" as saying that at least one of the United States thermonuclear explosions in that series employed the triggering method and material that had earlier been used in the Soviet Union.

Now that the race seems to be over, and there is talk of scratching all the horses, one may wonder whether Sakharov will ever come forth to claim from Edward Teller the controversial honor of being "Father of the Hydrogen Bomb."

CHAPTER 7

The Hidden
Universe

THIS chapter may be omitted by physicists, who are too familiar with modern physics and with Landau's contributions to it not to be irritated by unavoidable simplifications. It may be omitted also by those readers who are not physicists but who do not wish to be burdened with a few basic, if somewhat esoteric, concepts about matter, concepts that will be of no earthly use to them in their daily life.

Soviet physicists have been heard to remark, only half in jest, that "Dau discovered quantum mechanics and the principle of uncertainty when he was eighteen years old."

Of course Landau did not actually discover quantum mechanics, but he was probably one of the first physicists in the Soviet Union to plunge into it wholeheartedly when quantum mechanics was born, and certainly the first to grasp its importance fully and to accept it in spite of the ideologically motivated suspicion that first greeted the new science in the Soviet Union.

"Quantum mechanics and the principle of uncertainty are among the greatest triumphs of the human mind," Landau has said. "They go against everything that we have been used to believe in from our childhood. We see too big. None of us has ever seen an atom, and we do not even have any kind of inner feeling that can help us visualize atomic events. The discovery of quantum mechanics and of the principle of uncertainty has shown that man can tear himself away from deeply rooted notions, discover, and accept something that is beyond his power of visualizing."

From his youngest years as a student, Landau has contributed to so many facets of modern physics, that even physicists hesitate to say which was his most significant work, wavering between his theoretical description of superfluidity and his explanation of combined parity, or between his work in thermodynamics, and in ferromagnetism. A sampling of opinions in an attempt to list Landau's achievements in the order of their importance, indicates that his explanation of superfluidity (for which he was to receive the Nobel Prize) should come first, probably because Dau had, in fact, described a new state of matter, matter which behaves not like a solid or a gas, and not quite like an ordinary liquid either.

The first extensive, experimental study of superfluidity was undertaken by Piotr Kapitza in 1937, shortly after Landau had come to Moscow to direct the Theoretical Department of the Institute for Physical Problems. From his first experiments on, Kapitza found that superfluidity could give rise to just the type of situation that appealed to his flair for the spectacular, spurring him to almost feverish activity that often kept him up through the night, culminating in the design of new machinery and the achievement of unprecedented, sometimes incomprehensible results.

Superfluidity occurs when helium, a noninflammable, very light, chemically inactive gas found in the atmosphere in the proportion of about one in 200,000 parts, is cooled down to near absolute zero. (Absolute zero is considered as the lowest possible temperature for any element: $-459.69°$ F, or $-273.16°$ C. It was long assumed that at absolute zero all molecular motion would cease; Landau was one of the first to prove this assumption incorrect.)

When helium is refrigerated to minus $452°$F (slightly higher than absolute zero) it becomes a liquid. From experience with other elements, one would expect that if it were further cooled down, it would turn into a solid—but it doesn't. It changes, instead, into a "fourth state of matter", a kind of frictionless fluid, endowed with seemingly supernatural, rather spectacular properties:

If left in a glass, superfluid helium creeps up its sides, flows down the stem and spills out at the bottom.

When helium liquefies under refrigeration it starts bubbling like boiling water; but when it is cooled down even more, it suddenly becomes completely still.

Helium can flow out of a flask, yet the flask remains full!

In what is considered by physicists one of the most beautiful analyses of an experimental situation, Landau explained these strange properties, showing that liquid helium displays, on a large scale, the quantum properties of individual atoms and molecules, properties which are usually hidden, or "randomized," in a large mass. Though Landau's theory of superfluidity involves some rather complicated theoretical calculations, it is, basically, simple: it is as if liquid helium, the first "quantum liquid," were a mixture of two liquids, the "normal component," which behaves pretty much like an ordinary liquid, and the "superfluid component," which has no viscosity at all, opposing no resistence to flow. The superfluid component can be said to carry no heat at all, while the normal component does. The two can be mixed thoroughly and the concentration of one part to the other determines the average temperature of superfluid helium: the colder the mixture, the more superfluid component it contains, and vice versa. And because the superfluid part has no viscosity, the two components can flow in opposite directions, one through the other.

The fact that superfluid helium can spontaneously flow over the edge of a glass becomes understandable. Any liquid tends to adhere to a solid surface, forming a thin film of wetness. A person coming out of a bath is wet because of this adherence—otherwise, all of the water would immediately drip down from his skin. But it is not enough for a person to stand with his feet in a bathtub, to become completely wet: normal liquids are viscous, subjected to a drag that prevents the spontaneous formation of a film, particularly if this film has to creep upward against gravity.

But the film formed by superfluid helium, uninhibited by viscosity, can spread out freely, even upward against gravity. Thus when superfluid helium is poured into a glass, it immediately starts forming such a film which reaches up along the sides of the glass, goes over the rim and runs down its outer surface, forming a continuous, extremely thin flow, which siphons away liquid from the glass. As predicted by Landau, only the superfluid component flows out: This is confirmed by the fact that the less helium remains in the glass, the higher its temperature. When the temperature rises to the lambda point (the temperature above which liquid helium is no longer superfluid) the siphoning off ceases: only "normal" liquid helium remains in the container, and it is no longer endowed with superfluidity.

Landau's theory also explained how liquid helium can flow out of a flask, yet leave the flask full. This perplexing event was first observed by Kapitza, who had undertaken an experiment to show that in superfluid helium, heat was transported by the movement of the liquid itself, rather than by conductivity or radiation, the standard vehicles for heat transport.

At the opening of a flask, Kapitza installed a movable vane, so that any outflow of the liquid would deflect the vane outward. He filled the flask with liquid helium and plunged it into a vat-full of the same liquid. At first, the helium both in the flask and in the larger container were at the same temperature, and the vane did not budge. But when Kapitza heated the liquid in the flask, the vane was deflected outward: liquid helium flowed out as expected, transporting the increased temperature from the flask to the helium that surrounded it. But though the liquid was obviously flowing out, deflecting the vane, the astonished physicist saw that the flask remained full, and suspected at first that something had gone wrong with the experimental set-up.

But nothing had gone wrong. Landau's theory of superfluidity later explained what had happened: The liquid flowing out of the flask and transporting heat outward was of course the "normal component," the only one that can "contain heat." At the same time, the heatless, "superfluid component" was flowing from the vat into the flask, keeping the flask full. The vane at the neck of the flask was pushed outward by the outward flow of the normal component because that component has viscosity; but the inflowing superfluid component, having no viscosity, exerted no counteracting push on the vane at all. If the vane hadn't been there, one would have observed no motion of liquid, while in fact there were two currents of liquid flowing through each other in opposite directions.

The theory of superfluidity also explained why liquid helium, cooled down to the critical "lambda point," suddenly stops boiling and becomes absolutely still. Above the superfluid point, "normal" liquid helium boils because heat absorbed from the outside by the surface of the container causes some of the helium to evaporate along the walls and from the bottom, forming bubbles of gaseous helium which violently boil up, just as steam boils up from a kettlefull of water heated by a flame. But when helium becomes superfluid, the heat is transported away from the walls so fast (because it is transported by the rapid movement of the liquid itself, rather than by conductivity) that no bubbles are formed, and helium evaporates only at the surface of the vessel.

Not only did Landau's theory account for all of these strange properties of liquid helium that had been observed by experimental physicists, but it described another, that had never yet been observed. Since superfluid helium is capable of two simultaneous motions, Landau predicted that two different kinds of waves, moving at different speeds, could travel through the liquid. One type of wave would consist of vibrations of the superfluid component, the other, of vibrations in the normal one. If both components oscillated in unison and in the same direction, the result would be an ordinary sound wave, such as can occur in any liquid. According to Landau's theory, however, vibrations in the superfluid component should be out of phase with vibrations in the normal one, and there should be a "second sound."

Experiments were undertaken at the Institute for Physical Problems to verify this prediction. They consisted of originating a sound in a vat of superfluid helium, and attempting to detect the sound signals at some distance away. But throughout several experiments, only one signal could be picked up—and a weak one at that. It seemed that Landau had been wrong—until his friend, Yevgheni Lifshitz, found the answer: Normally, sound waves are propagated in the form of compressions and rarefactions, which move through gas, liquids or solids. However, if two media oscillate in opposite directions, the compressions and rarefactions almost completely cancel each other. This must have happened in superfluid helium, and Lifshitz suggested another experiment to confirm the existence of the second sound, using, instead of sound waves, temperature waves in which the successions of "ups and downs" of temperature play the role of "ups and downs" of pressure. The results of the experiment confirmed Landau's prediction, quantitatively as well as qualitatively. The second sound wave arises when the temperature of helium reaches the superfluid point, and its velocity increases as temperature goes down. At two degrees centigrade above absolute zero, the speed of the second sound is around 60 feet per second, and it goes up to about 120 feet per second at 0.5°. Normally, the speed of sound is hardly affected by temperature at all.

Since Landau developed the theory of superfluidity in 1941, it has been experimentally verified the world over, and in recent years cryogenics—the study of matter at extremely low temperature—has become an essential tool for theoretical research and its practical applications. Just as superfluid helium has no viscosity, or no drag, a number of metals refrigerated to very low temperature lose resistance to the passage of electrical current and become "superconductors" of electricity. Liquid helium is used as a cooling medium in the design of "cryogenic computers" which can make calculations incomparably faster than ordinary electronic computers. Superconductors can magnify electrical effects, achieving such results as the design of an electromagnet weighing one pound which can be more powerful than an ordinary magnet weighing 20 tons.

Helium being the only element which reaches the state of superfluidity instead of becoming solidified at extremely low temperature, studies have also been made of Helium 3, a rare isotope of Helium 4. (Helium 4 is the "natural" helium first studied by Kapitza and Landau.) Helium 3 can also become a quantum liquid, displaying unusual properties, though it does not, like Helium 4, become superfluid.

Next to the analysis and explanation of this "new state of matter" of helium, one of Landau's most important contributions to modern physics is a theory which has to do with one of the basic laws of nature, that of symmetry between right and left.

The existence of this symmetry in nature may seem self-evident. It is common sense, for example, that if the laws of physics allow motion from left to right, they also allow motion from right to left, the second being the mirror image of the first. This is particularly evident because the concepts of right and left are not absolute but are only defined with reference to some particular observer or object. The same can be said of clockwise or counter-clockwise motion. The hands of a clock seen in a mirror would appear to be running counterclockwise; but so they would also appear if the clock were transparent and viewed from behind.

However, some aspects of right and left *are* absolute. Consider, for example, an ordinary screw. Screws are usually made to be "right-handed," that is, to be screwed in with a clockwise motion of a screwdriver. No matter the position of an observer, a right-handed screw will always be a right-handed screw. It is only the mirror image of such a screw that becomes fundamentally different: it is a left-handed screw, with grooves placed in such a way that it would be screwed in with a counterclockwise motion of the screwdriver.

In short, the principle of conservation of parity reflects the absence, in nature, of a preference for either right-handed or left-handed screws. On the nuclear scale, the equivalent of a screw could be, for instance, the direction of the spin of a particle ejected during a nuclear interaction. It has long been taken for granted that for each physical process there existed—or could, in principle, exist—the mirror-image process. This means, for instance, that if a film was taken showing the interaction of nuclear particles, the images could be turned around before a showing so that right becomes left and vice versa, and still the viewer would see the picture of a true physical event. (This is not to be taken to mean that the film should be run backward—that operation would illustrate the time-reversal transformation, which is quite a different matter.)

All of the experiments involving electromagnetic or strong nuclear interactions seemed to confirm the existence of parity, and physicists did not doubt that the law of conservation of parity was valid also for any other type of physical event.

In 1956, Tsung Dao Lee and Chen Ning Yang, two physicists who had emigrated from China to the United States, pointed out that parity had never been tested for weak interactions, and suggested a disturbing hypothesis: the two types of mesons were actually one and the same particle, which could break up, or decay, in violation of the principle of conservation of parity. They suggested an experiment, which was performed by Chien Shung Wu and showed that, indeed, parity appeared to break down in certain weak interactions: the collision debris had a right or left preference, whereas the principle of conservation of parity decreed that no such preference could exist.

This came down to admitting that in the world of weak interactions, there could exist only right-handed screws and no left-handed ones, or vice versa. It followed that there was no strict symmetry of space, but instead, an occasional preference for right-handedness or left-handedness. Madame Wu's experiment, in fact, not only overthrew the principle of parity, but threatened existing theories on physical events and on the properties of space. (For this overthrow, Lee and Yang were rewarded with the Nobel Prize.)

Madame Wu, called upon to present the results of her work at an international gathering of physicists, commented that she had come to the meeting "on the strength of the weak interaction," and Edgar Okonov, a researcher at the Dubna atomic center near Moscow, later summed-up the general conscensus that "all in all, weak interactions dealt out a crashing blow to two fundamental symmetry laws." Like Damocles' sword, parity overthrown threat-

eningly hung over fundamental notions of modern physics.

Lev Davidovich Landau, working independently in
Moscow, approached the problem in his usual fashion: "If
you want to answer a question, start working from the
basic principles," he used to say. In this case, the basic
premise was that laws of nature could not depend on a
human convention, such as the distinction between right
and left. Therefore, he argued, if a violation of parity
occurs, it has to be compensated by the violation of some
other convention in such a way that both cancel each
other out, and that the resulting phenomenon is again
"natural."

The simplest assumption was that the other violation
would be that of charge symmetry, according to which all
physical laws would remain valid if all particles were replaced by "anti-particles" of opposite electrical charge,
and Landau developed a theory according to which the
two violations—that of parity and of charge symmetry—
could not occur independently of each other. In other
words, Landau theorized that parity is conserved in weak
(and other) interactions, provided that the particles are
replaced by anti-particles which have opposite electrical
charges. He developed this hypothesis mathematically,
and suggested experiments to verify it. "Combined parity"
was confirmed by a number of experiments, notably at
Dubna, where it was shown that combined parity was conserved in K meson decay, in spite of the violation of both
charge and reflection symmetries. Landau's principle of
combined parity restored the isotropy of space that had
been violated by Lee and Yang.

Among Landau's contributions to physics, there also
stands out his work (in which he was partly seconded by
Lifshitz) in thermodynamics, the study of the laws gov-

erning processes of heat changes, where he made a very thorough analysis of the complicated phenomena which occur when two phases of a substance are formed and have to arrange themselves in more or less stable configurations. Landau's former colleague Professor Leon Rosenfeld notes, in particular, that

he has unravelled, notably, the very complicated structure of the so-called "domains" of uniform magnetization in ferromagnetic substances, and the still more complicated arrangement of superconductive and non-superconductive domains in superconductive material of arbitrary shape. He has also given a most beautiful analysis of the fluctuation around the equilibrium analysis. And his work in electromagnetic theory, especially in collaboration with Peierls, played an important part in the elucidation of the fundamental properties of the quantum theory of radiation.

The last few years before his accident, Landau had become increasingly concerned with the need for an entirely new approach to the understanding of the physical world. By now, he pointed out, more than thirty subatomic particles have been observed, and each has its corresponding anti-particle of opposite electrical charge. "But this accumulation of knowledge has led physicists into a dead end. Some of the actual theories are contradictory, and don't explain *why* particles are such as they are—they only define them on the basis of experimental work. The properties of particles, their mass and charge, must cease to be experimental facts only. One should be able to say why, for instance, the proton has a mass of nearly two thousand times that of the electron, and why there is no particle that has, say, half the mass of an electron. Why is it that some particles, which logically could exist, are not found in nature?"

Science has much growing to do, both in width and in

depth, Landau commented. The explanation of concrete events may be described as the growth of science in width: an example would be the increased understanding of life processes in nature: "There is not the slightest doubt that we already know with the highest degree of precision all of the basic physical laws which underlie these life processes," Landau maintained. "In the end of ends, all of these processes are extremely complex manifestations of events on the atomic and molecular scale. But no matter how complex and specialized, these events are in the last resort submitted to the laws which rule the world of atoms and molecules—the laws of quantum mechanics. There is nothing mystic in life processes. However, neither biophysicists nor biochemists can say that they understand deeply the mechanisms of these processes. The path from the basic laws of nature to the building of a biophysical theory, which could be called the theory of life, is far from covered. The building of such a theory will require an immense joint effort of many researchers in different fields."

Then, there is the growth of science in depth: It is the establishment of new basic laws. "We all know, of course, that atomic nuclei contain protons and neutrons, the basic structural elements of the nucleus," Landau once told a group of Soviet science writers. "The unusually strong forces between these elements have led to the comparison of atomic nuclei to impregnable castles, because nuclear bonds are thousands of times stronger than electromagnetic forces. This difference in quantitative strength also has enormous qualitative significance: theories which were so powerful in explaining electromagnetic events are almost completely powerless in the realm of nuclear interactions."

Landau believed that the trouble lay not so much in the shortcomings of the outward, formal mathematical expression of nuclear theory, as in its depth: "Apparently, in our physical outlook, some still unknown general laws of nature have not been taken into consideration. . . . Properties of particles must become the consequences of some laws of the existence of matter. So far, theoretical physicists have not found these laws."

"It is difficult, of course, to predict the future," said Landau after the International Congress on High Energy Particles held in Kiev in 1959, during which he had made one of the shortest reports, containing not a single formula but attempting to peer into the crystal ball and to establish a general program for future research. "There is nothing surprising in the fact that different physicists take entirely different positions as far as their hopes and expectations are concerned. I am fairly optimistic and believe that a new theory is not far behind the mountains, and will exist, in a few years, in a more or less usable form."

A new theory, however, cannot be built on old ideas and without completely new concepts, he insisted. "Every noticeable step forward in physics is linked with the denial of some of our usual representations about the way things are in nature. Einstein's theory of relativity, for instance, forced physicists to deny that there was an absolute time, even though the belief in absolute time had existed for thousands of years. Of course, the theory of relativity first seemed insane. Quantum mechanics required another denial—that of our usual representation and understanding of the *nature* of physical bodies. All of the psychological trauma connected with the acceptance of the theory of relativity was but childish concern when it came to accepting the wild ideas of quantum mechanics. Even today, it seems insane to someone who is not a physicist, to say that a particle, moving from one region of space to another, does not follow any particular trajectory. This just doesn't seem to agree with healthy common sense."

Landau even advanced, during the Kiev congress, some ideas about how this theory would be reached and what shape it might take. (Needless to say, his ideas were hotly disputed by many physicists, among them Werner Heisenberg, who greeted "with pleasure the revolutionary spirit of the Landau program," adding: "My path I consider more conservative, but I suppose that conservatism must be feared more than revolutionarism.")

When he later explained his views to a lay audience, Landau said: "I think that the future theory will reject the examination of the process of interaction between particles. It will show that in this process there are no exactly definable characteristics, even in terms of quantum mechanical precision. Description of the process of interaction is an illusion, just as classical trajectories turned out to be illusions."

Landau suggested that, instead, the new theory would examine the behavior of particles *before* and *after* interaction:

"Physicists have learned that certain questions cannot be asked, not because the level of our knowledge does not yet permit us to find the answer, but because such an answer simply isn't stored in nature. This rejection of earlier ideas will of course be accompanied by the appearance of new ones, truer ones, and therefore, more fruitful ones.

"If my idea is right—and I, of course, believe it is—this now developing theory will make it clear that nature is made up in an even more clever way than we now think it is.

"This should not surprise anyone. Imagine how strange it would be if all of nature were organized in the image of the experiences we acquire by walking along the street, by bathing in water, and other everyday events of human life. . . . Nature would seem extremely flat and vulgar, if these classical organic experiences of ours were applicable to all of its manifestations."

CHAPTER 8

As Long as
There Is Life

(JANUARY 7–JANUARY 11, 1962)

ON SUNDAY morning, January 7, 1962, Landau's un-recognizeable, blood-stained body lay stretched out on the operating table in an emergency room at the Timiriasevsky District Hospital in suburban Moscow. Dr. Nina Yegorova, assistant to the hospital's chief physician, examined the massive injuries suffered by the scientist in the smashup on Dimitrovsky Highway a few minutes earlier.

The fracture of the skull, the broken ribs piercing the lungs, the shattered pubic bones or the torn internal organs —each of these injuries alone could be mortal. The dark-haired, matronly physician, a white hospital gown over her house-dress, had little doubt that the illustrious life of a man she knew only by reputation had come to an abrupt end.

Vladimir Sudakov, the driver of the fateful car, was so

despondent with grief and guilt that he was unable to speak coherently. He was driven to the Institute of Physical Problems, where veteran physicist Piotr Kapitza and many of Landau's friends had their apartments. Physicists at the institute decided to keep Sudakov under surveillance, fearing he would take his own life if Landau died.

Dau's students and friends started seeking each other out in their homes, in theaters, restaurants, in country *dachas* outside of Moscow, leaving whatever they were doing in the hope that they could be of some help at the hospital. Dau's wife Cora learned of the accident in the country home to which she had taken their fifteen-year-old son, Igor, for the weekend. When she arrived at the hospital in the afternoon, her strikingly beautiful face stained with tears, such a large group of friends and so many cars had gathered in the street that the *militia*, the city police, was on hand to keep a clear path for ambulances. Physicists, who had taken over the office of the hospital director, first tried to keep Cora from the sight of her husband's seemingly lifeless body, but no argument could prevail. Always highly emotional and now near hysterics, Cora fainted at the sight of Dau's ashen face, his head covered with bandages, his glassy eyes open, motionlessly staring ahead into nothingness. When she came to, surrounded by many of her husband's devoted friends, she had to be almost forcibly persuaded to return to the country to keep Igor away from Moscow for a few days.

Landau's friends remember these few hours after the accident in a confused way, as one remembers a nightmare from which one has only an obscure hope of awakening. They were driven by the thought that they should do something to help, but they didn't know what

to do. Several of them decided to seek out medical specialists who, they thought, might be needed in the struggle
that was taking shape. But they were too stunned to be
organized. By late in the afternoon more than twenty
physicians had gathered at the Timiriasevsky District
Hospital. They stood in small groups in the corridors, har-
assed by the physicists who asked them to perform a
miracle, hesitant to pronounce themselves on a case such
as had not been known to survive. Some of Dau's students
came to the doctors crying openly, pleading that they do
something—when in fact, there was not much to do but
wait. Landau's superficial wounds had been dressed, and
he was taken to a quiet room on the hospital's top floor.

One of the physicians who arrived at the hospital that
Sunday afternoon was Professor Nikolai Ivanovich Grashchenkov, one of the Soviet Union's top neuropathologists,
the head of a neurological hospital, full member of the
Academy of Medical Sciences and corresponding member
of the Academy of Sciences of the U.S.S.R. Silently bent
over Landau's bloodless, gray face, the tall, quiet physician took his pulse, tried without success to elicit a muscular reflex, thoughtfully examined the medical reports,
and asked a few questions. Then he stood up. "Let's have
a talk," he said to the physicians who surrounded him.

At four in the afternoon, the first of what was to be a
long series of conferences took place in a small whitewashed room on the hospital's sixth floor, down the hall
from where Landau lay motionless under the watchful
eyes of nurses. Physicist Yevgheni Lifshitz, Landau's
former student and his closest friend, sat in with the doctors, wearing a white hospital gown.

What was to be done? Such was the extent of injuries
that all of the physicians rapidly agreed that active treat-

ment should at first be avoided. Any major surgery, any attempt even at resetting the broken bones into their natural position, would be an additional trauma that could be fatal. This "wait-and-see" attitude, however, could be extremely dangerous, particularly with respect to one organ, in which the extent of damage could not be assessed from outward signs: the brain.

The brain's existence barely manifested itself. The fact that Landau breathed, however irregularly, indicated that at least part of the brain, that concerned with the maintenance and control of the "automatic" vital functions, was in working condition. The "higher" brain centers in the principal brain stem, the cortex, showed no sign of existence at all. Reflexes were nonexistent: the pricking with a needle caused no pain reaction at all, the eyes stared blankly and motionlessly, unblinking even at the flashing of a light. It was probable that many cerebral vessels had been torn, and that fluids accumulated inside the skull exerted increasing pressure and threatened further damage.

If a large, local accumulation of blood existed, forming a hematoma, a blood-swollen tumor, it should be removed whatever the risk before it grew enough to cause more extensive damage. But then perhaps there was no hematoma, noted Grashchenkov, but rather, a number of small hemorrhages, resulting from the breaking of tiny blood vessels, that may have temporarily increased pressure in the skull, but which could not be surgically removed and should be left alone, hopefully to disappear with time. "One doesn't shoot sparrows with a cannon," as Grashchenkov put it.

After examining the patient several times, the brain specialists felt they could no longer postpone their choice between one calculated risk and another. In spite of the additional trauma, an exploratory craniotomy was decided upon. Landau's motionless body was wheeled out into the nearest operating room. Three of the Soviet Union's top neurosurgeons prepared themselves for the operation: Professor Joseph Irger, to be assisted by Professors Grigori Kornyansky and Sergei Fyodorov.

Landau was covered with white sheets, leaving only a small square section of the shaven skull exposed, on which a tiny blue circle was drawn. In the silence of the hospital at night, nurses in the hall could hear the brief, muffled noise of the drill attacking bone. Minutes later, the tiny trepanation was completed. Irger, Kornyansky and Fyodorov examined the neat opening, from which the light, clear cerebrospinal fluid that surrounds the organs of the central nervous system, had started oozing. There was hardly any blood at all. No hematoma was apparent, at least not in the frontal part of the skull that had been selected for the operation, as the most likely to have suffered severe damage. "This looks good," said Kornyansky. "But remember—we cannot be absolutely sure that a hematoma has not formed in some other part of the brain."

Landau was returned to his room, and the first nightwatch prepared for a long wait. Dr. Fyodorov, staff surgeon at the Burdenko Neurosurgical Institute, volunteered to remain, together with Victor Luchkow, a young practitioner who, from then on, did not leave the hospital for several weeks.

Night had fallen on Moscow. Even the dim echoes of the radio playing in apartment houses near the hospital had faded away, and only now and then the grinding of a truck slowly passing in the street interrupted the silence.

In the hospital director's room there remained a group of physicists who had decided to stay through to the morning, placing themselves at the disposal of the medical team. Cars waited in the courtyard. Nurses dozed. Irochka, a pretty young girl who had joined the hospital's staff a few weeks earlier, busied herself in the kitchen preparing tea which she took around to the physicists and doctors who were staying awake.

From Landau's bed there came the faint, irregular but reassuring noise of breathing, sometimes a grating sound, like a weak cough. The physicist was still alive, and hope grew. Now and then the men who watched over him stood up to stretch, walking down the corridor, trying to answer endless questions from the physicists, or listening to their admiring remarks about "their Landau," memories brought from the past as they are when somebody is dead.

It was almost three in the morning when Luchkow, his young face heavy with sleepiness, jumped up from his chair and leaned over Landau. "Listen," he said. Fyodorov was intent. A choking noise came from the motionless figure, so thin under the blankets that it could have been a child. Then, silence.

"He has stopped breathing . . . Tracheotomy!" snapped Fyodorov. Two nurses already stood by his side. The trachea, leading air into the lungs, was blocked. Landau did not have the normal, strong coughing reflex to clear his throat, and the weak motions of the chest could not force the obstruction through. Cyanosis rapidly set in: the accumulation of dark blood, deprived of life-giving oxygen, was giving the pale, yellowish face a dark, bluish hue.

With a slow, deliberate motion of the scalpel, Fyodorov

made an incision across Landau's throat below the Adam's apple. There was no need for anesthesia—the physicist was far beyond the reach of pain. The skin parted neatly and Fyodorov found the trachea, easily accessible in the lean, fat-free body. Another incision, and a bubbling of black blood rapidly swabbed away. Abandoning the scalpel, Fyodorov reached for a plastic tube that was thrust into his hand, introduced it into the trachea. "The respirator," he ordered. A rubber balloon (normally used for anesthesia during surgery) was connected to the tube and Fyodorov squeezed it slowly by hand, one, two, three times . . .

Immediately the chest heaved, audibly sucking in air through the tube. Almost instantly the face pinkened as the heart beat hungrily for the oxygen that returned strength to its starved muscles. The entire drama of life and death had not lasted for more than two minutes. The tracheal catheter was now firmly implanted, secured to the throat by antiseptic gauze. After the first gasps for life, the respirator bag was removed, and breathing settled to a quiet, reassuring rhythm.

Unable to sleep, Luchkow and Fyodorov sat up to see the gray cold dawn come up over Moscow, listening to the awakening of the city, sipping the endless cups of weak tea that Russians are so fond of. "Well, Irochka, we made it," smiled Fyodorov as the young girl removed the cups once more.

Soon Landau's friends started arriving, sometimes alone, sometimes bringing along a physician, sometimes in small groups. By nine in the morning a grouchy nurse protested that the comrades should stop throwing their coats around, and ordered that a special coat-rack be provided for Landau's visitors.

This day of January 8, 1962, was to see the birth of an organization probably unprecedented in the history of man's humanity to man. More than a hundred physicists and physicians, fueled with new hope, started joining forces to save the life of a man so many loved and admired. Professor Grashchenkov, who had never met Landau personally, only then realized how much devotion the scientist commanded. His students and friends had suddenly become an almost irresistible force, that could bring to Landau's bedside practically any specialist in Moscow. Lifshitz, whose wife was a pathologist and anatomist, Kapitza, whose status and reputation gave him access to anyone at any level, and scores of other physicists were ready to abandon their work and to go to any extreme, if it helped save their friend. Such was their enthusiasm, such also was Landau's fame, that no one who was asked to help ever refused.

Under Professor Grashchenkov, a unique medical team started taking shape. "Let's not draft all of the Soviet doctors," commented the tall, debonair neurologist, faced by a barrage of suggestions that would have all but emptied Moscow's hospitals, as he started preparing a coherent list of specialists who might, at one time or another, be needed. Professor Boris Yegorov, director of the Burdenko Institute of Neurosurgery, one of the top Soviet neurosurgeons, had already been contacted and came at the head of the list. There were neurosurgeon Grigori Kornyanski, and Professor Valentin Polyakoff, surgeon and traumatologist; microbiologist Zinaida Yermoleyeva, a specialist on antibiotics; Alim Damir and Joseph Kassirsky, therapists and specialists in internal medicine; neuropathologist Mikhail Rappaport, Vera Dubrovskaya, and respiration specialist Lyubov Popova; surgeon Sergei Fyodorov, whose intervention had already saved Landau's life; and Doctor Victor Luchkow, who became Landau's permanent personal physician. The team included orthopedists, blood specialists, nephrologists, nutritionists, urologists, pharmacologists, experts in nearly every medical specialty, who could be called at a moment's notice, whenever their knowledge would be needed to help reach one of the many therapeutical decisions that would undoubtedly have to be taken if Landau survived. "I don't think such a team ever existed before," Grashchenkov later commented. "From the human viewpoint this was, of course, an exceptional example of devotion. From the medical viewpoint, I think it was unprecedented. Just imagine . . . isn't it a doctor's dream, to have at his disposal, as consultants for a single patient, the best specialists in his country?"

To back up and encourage the medical team, physicists also organized a group designed to be ready to provide, with the least possible delay, any service that could be requested by the doctors—and more. "We made a duty roster of volunteers—and when I counted up the names, there were eighty-nine of them," remembers Aleksei Abrikossov—Landau's favorite student "Aliosha," now one of the youngest professors of theoretical physics in the Soviet Union.

"First, we organized a permanent watch, so that a few physicists would always be at the hospital, with a car waiting in the courtyard. Irochka's full-time assistance was drafted—without any difficulty, such was her willingness to help us. Lifshitz and his wife became the liaison with the medical team, giving us frequent reports on Dau's condition, so that we wouldn't pester the doctors all the time. Those who had cars became chauffeurs, ready to pick up doctors or bring them home at any time of the day or night." Abrikossov himself took the night shift, transfering some of his books and papers to the hospital, where he continued to work.

Sergei Kapitza, the son of the director of the Institute for Physical Problems, and an experimental physicist himself, was approached to install a private telephone for Landau's doctors. "You're an experimentalist, and a *shishka*" (meaning "hump"—the Russian colloquialism equivalent to "big wheel"). "You can do it faster than any of us," he was told. Sergei rushed off, returning an hour later with a telephone he had requisitioned somewhere, dragging along rolls of wire, and an electrician he had drafted for the occasion. Without requesting official permission, which might have wasted a few hours, Sergei strung an outside wire from Landau's room on the sixth floor to the hospital switchboard below, installed a priority telephone and firmly instructed the bewildered hospital operator to let calls on this line be made anywhere, in the Soviet Union or abroad.

Sergei's father, Piotr Kapitza, in the meanwhile called or wired Landau's friends—Pat Blackett in Oxford, Niels Bohr in Copenhagen, and scientists throughout the Soviet Union, telling them of the accident and warning them that he might call again to request medicine or other assistance if any were needed.

Meanwhile several bedside conferences had been held at the hospital, to follow, hour after hour, Landau's condition. Dau remained completely unconscious, but continued to breathe on his own, through the tube in his trachea. Antibiotics were injected to prevent infection of his wound, and a nutrient solution introduced into his veins.

It was in the morning of January 9 that the medical team was faced with the first of many crucial problems it would have to solve. Pressure from the cerebro-spinal fluid was building up inside Landau's skull. If it weren't checked, the pressure might squeeze the vessels of the cerebral circulation, and lead to the destruction of portions of the brain by starvation. Specialists urged that the pressure be relieved by one of several substances that can be introduced into the brain to "dry-up" excessive fluids —substances such as urea, manathol, or glucose. They ordered that several sample injections be prepared, in case one or another became necessary—and it turned out that urea was not readily available.

Piotr Kapitza, who was at the hospital, understood that there was none in Moscow, and wired Blackett in London, requesting that a sufficient supply be shipped by the first plane to Moscow. In Blackett's absence the cable was delivered to physicist Sir John Cockroft, who immediately telephoned Sir Harold Himmsworth, secretary of the British Medical Research Council. Sir Harold suggested that a new British drug, Ureaphil, be used. A package was made up, addressed simply to "Landau, Moscow," and driven to London airport. As there was no immediate flight for the Soviet Union, the medicine was handed to a passenger on the Warsaw plane. In Warsaw, Soviet officials, alerted by telephone, met the plane and transferred the package to a Moscow-bound liner. At Moscow International Airport, a physicist on duty had already contacted customs officials and when the package arrived (on the same day Kapitza had sent his wire) he was waiting near the landing strip. The soldier who was to check the passengers' passports first called for the parcel, which was driven to the hospital—no doubt the fastest door-to-door delivery service ever achieved between London and Moscow. Ironically, by the time Ureaphil arrived, pure urea had turned out to be plentiful in the Leningrad Neurosurgical Institute, from which it had already been flown to Moscow.

The pressure on the brain was relieved—but another, perplexing observation was made shortly thereafter. In spite of massive administration of antibiotics to prevent infection of Landau's wounds, the infections persisted and threatened to spread. Antibiotics specialists had no explanation for the apparent ineffectiveness of the preparations that had been injected, until Professor Grashchenkov learned that Landau had long been an indiscriminate, almost addicted user of antibiotics, which he took against colds and other minor ailments that could easily have been treated without them. As a result, he had become almost immune to the therapeutic action of the most current Soviet antibiotics, with which his organism and the bacteria it contained were so familiar. (His was not an uncommon habit, noted Grashchenkov. Pusillanimous patients often do not realize that they can build up so strong an immunity that in an emergency, current antibiotics become ineffective).

It was clear that an entirely new spectrum of antibiotics was urgently needed for Landau. Zinaida Yermoleyevna and Grashchenkov compiled a list of foreign preparations, and handed it to Kapitza and to Lifshitz. Kapitza again wired abroad, while Lifshitz telephoned Robert Maxwell in Oxford, who was the publisher of several English translations of Landau's work.

Maxwell, formerly Jan Ludwig Hoch, had come to England as a boy soldier in the Czech Army in 1940, had been assigned intelligence work, and won the Military Cross at war's end. Later he became engaged in publishing, scoring a coup when he flew to Moscow to promote the exchange of books between Russia and the West. He spoke fluent Russian and had met Landau, Kapitza, and Lifshitz several times. Moreover, when Lifshitz called him, fate had already made him familiar with the type of medicine that might be needed in such a case: A few days earlier Maxwell's seventeen-year-old son, Paul André, was a passenger in a car that had collided with a truck, and had since been in a coma. Maxwell's son had not recovered, and his physicians did not believe he ever would.

Robert Maxwell knew only too well what might be needed for Landau, and where to find it rapidly. Four of the six antibiotics requested were available in London, and on the same day he received Lifshitz' call, Maxwell succeeded in detaining a British Comet airliner about to take off from London to Moscow. The antibiotics were handed to the pilot, and at the Moscow International Airport, a physicist was waiting again as the jet rolled to a stop, to drive the medicine to the hospital.

The request for another drug was telephoned to New York. The American antibiotic was being flown to Moscow, and the sixth and last was on its way from Brussels. Every day, packages addressed to Landau kept coming to Sheremetevo airport near Moscow from Britain, the United States, Germany, Czechoslovakia, Denmark, and Belgium. At the airport, there was always a physicist, sometimes a world-renowned theoretician or experimentalist, ready to rush the drug to the hospital.

Infection was checked—but Landau continued to sink.

On the night of January 9, Professor Alim Damir sat at his bedside, listening to the superficial, rapid, irregular respiration when suddenly, without any warning, breathing stopped completely.

This had been expected to happen sooner or later. The medical team had already told the physicians that an artificial breathing apparatus should be on hand. From the Moscow Institute of Cardiac Surgery, physicists had lugged a Swedish Angstrom respirator and, on second thought, returned to pick up another that was available, just in case the first one failed. To be completely insured against mechanical failure, they even drafted a specialized repairman, who was ready to rush to the hospital on the shortest notice.

Breathing stopped at three in the morning, recalls Professor Damir. Perhaps because the broken ribs and torn lungs now caused so much irritation that all connections to the brain were defensively cut off—even those leading to the center which controls respiration, normally an automatic, subconscious process.

Without the loss of more than a few seconds, a respirator bag (the same type that had been used two days earlier) was first connected to the tracheal catheter, and regularly squeezed by hand while the respirator was connected, not only to breathe for Landau, but to evacuate liquids that might otherwise accumulate in his bronchia, the subdivisions of the windpipe in lungs. Once more the scientist's life had been saved—but a new threat soon became evident.

The breathing rate in man and animal is controlled by the brain, which receives information from the body, integrates it, and appropriately controls the rate and depth of inspirations and expirations to maintain a regular proportion of oxygen in arterial blood. (This proportion is expressed in "percentage of saturation": normally, arterial human blood, returning from the lungs, should be at 96 percent saturation, i.e., contain 96 percent of the maximum amount of oxygen that could be dissolved in it.)

During heavy physical exercise, breathing becomes deeper and more rapid, not necessarily because one consciously wants to breathe fast, but because instructions in the form of nervous impulses come from the breathing center in the medulla, the portion of the brain below the main brain stem, which tapers down into the vertebral column.

In the case of Landau, the automatic control of oxygen saturation had ceased. It had to be carried out artificially by regulating the respirator, increasing or decreasing the amount of oxygen pumped into his lungs. How much oxygen should be given was determined, more or less empirically, from his symptoms and from frequent blood tests. The task was complicated by the rupture of several vessels in his thoracic cage. Blood saturation dropped to as low as 40 percent, less than half the normal.

Still further complications came from wild variations of temperature. The breakdown of cells in the body is accompanied by increased metabolism—the sum of the physical and chemical processes maintained in the organism—and by rising temperature. High temperature required the burning of a larger amount of oxygen to fuel the overactive organism—thus a person with high temperature breathes faster than normally, increasing oxygen intake. In the case of Landau, this adjustment could be made only artificially, by stepping up the oxygen supply and the tempo of the respirator when temperature rose— and it went up to as high as 107.5°F, never falling below 104°.

Another growing threat came from the lesions in Landau's abdomen and pelvis. The extent and nature of these injuries were not known, but abdominal functions were completely arrested. Landau was fed through his veins, with proteins and sugars that could be directly assimilated into the blood. The abdomen was increasingly distended but had not been siphoned off yet because any motion of the body could aggravate the fractures and the damage to internal organs.

Internal functions were so disturbed that there started a self-poisoning of the body, an autointoxication resulting from the organism's inability to control metabolism and elimination of waste products. No matter how balanced the minerals, how pure the carbohydrates introduced into the veins, this type of feeding was nowhere as adequate as if the food were screened by the digestive system itself. The body needed electrolytes, solutions that conduct electricity by means of ions. It needed "trace minerals" such as potassium, sodium or magnesium, but in minute amounts only; their excess could be fatal. (Potassium, for instance, is vital to the heart's rhythm, but can be particularly toxic if introduced in excessive amounts. The equilibrium between the electrolytes must be so precise, that even a fatal imbalance often goes unnoticed until it is too late.)

The prolonged artificial feeding could not but result in a dangerous disproportion of proteins in the blood, the accumulation of waste products from destroyed cells, and a wavering acid-base balance, all of which had to be detected every two or three hours by an examination of the fractions of the blood, and compensated either by the injection of missing substances, or by mass transfusion of donor blood. Blood donors were not lacking: all the physicists "on duty" were ready to volunteer, and several whose blood group was the same as Landau's had been selected and advised to eat much *bifshtek*.

Finally, on the fourth day after the accident, kidney

function failed. The kidneys could no longer keep up with the elimination of toxic substances from the blood. Their accumulation caused a general edema, the swelling of the entire body. The onslaught of death persisted from every side. Infection did not disappear completely, temperature continued to exhaust the heart, and arterial pressure wavered wildly.

During the third and fourth day after the accident, physicians gathered at Landau's bedside at least every hour. Several stayed through the night, taking short naps in neighboring rooms, on chairs, couches or stretchers. Sometimes, more than a dozen hands were busy at once keeping the spark of life in the body of Lev Davidovich Landau, a body which, by all medical standards, should have been already lifeless.

In the afternoon of the fourth day, temperature rose again to a peak of 107.5°, and the heart fluttered. In the hall outside of Landau's room, Dr. Nina Yegorova saw a wearied, unshaven Grashchenkov. "Landau's face is absolutely livid. Pulse has just stopped, arterial tension dropped to zero, the heart no longer beats, and even his pupils don't react to light," he said tonelessly, leaning in the doorway.

It was January 11. Landau had entered the state of "clinical death." His first death—but not his last.

CHAPTER 9

"Death has so many doors to let out life…"

(JANUARY 11-FEBRUARY 26, 1962)

FOUR days had passed since the accident, and at the Timiriasevky District Hospital in Moscow, Lev Davidovich Landau now lay dead.

He was dead, in the full meaning of the word as it is pronounced by medical science, authoritatively perhaps but with the reservation of someone venturing upon thin ice: "Death," as medical dictionaries tersely put it, "is the apparent extinction of life, as manifested by absence of heartbeat and respiration." Landau was not breathing, and his heart no longer beat.

But aside from this brief definition, which isn't really one, what is death? Is death the sudden onslaught of nothingness in that fleeting moment when the spark of life, the soul, leaves the body? Can death be half-a-death, slowly creeping in the body until it reaches a sort of point of no return, after which life no longer can exist?

It is ironical that poets and philosophers have given their many answers but that hardly any of those people who live in the constant presence of death—the physicians, the biologists, and the priests, who deal with death day after day—have gone much further than to observe, when the time seemed appropriate, that "life has become apparently extinct," or that "the soul has left its mortal dwelling."

Modern science has probed into, and often achieved, deep understanding of such occult riddles as heredity or the structure of matter, but it has made no unreserved attempt to understand death. In medicine, the realm of specialization, there are no "necrologists" or specialists in death, though death itself is a significant clinical event destined to come as a conclusion to every patient's medical record. But death is also a social impropriety, a taboo of all times and almost all peoples, surrounded with emotional undertones that seem to make a study of death inappropriate. Death is a fearful event that it is more convenient not to think about.

> The weariest and most loathed wordly life
> That age, ache, penury, and imprisonment
> Can lay on nature, is a paradise
> To what we fear of death

wrote Shakespeare. And Browning,

> Fear Death? To feel the fog in my throat,
> The mist in my face.

Even in our enlightened times, a physician pronouncing a man dead or, more cautiously, apparently dead, establishes his diagnosis on foggy and misty notions. Folklore—and coroners' reports—are full of stories about corpses arising from under the white sheet to frighten (to death perhaps) morgue attendants or funeral parlor clerks. Many examples have shown the existence of a goodly margin of human error, where death is not so final, and tales of horror in the best tradition are often based on fact.

More significant from a scientific viewpoint, however, is the story of the death of a Russian soldier on the German front during World War II, for his story marks a turning point in the study of death.

On the third of March 1943, Private Valentin Zderepanov was struck in the chest by a small shell fragment which opened his thoracic cage, tore into his lungs, and severed the aorta, the big artery distributing fresh blood from the heart to the body. There was no breathing, no pulse, and no heartbeat when a frontline medic collected Zderepanov's identification tag, signed the death certificate, and went on with his heartbreaking business.

Now, every March third, Zderepanov opens a few bottles of vodka and Soviet champagne to celebrate the anniversary of his death—a celebration occasionally shared by one Professor Vladimir Negovsky.

Since 1936, Dr. Negovsky had been an assistant to Professor Bruchanenko of Moscow, who was studying the process of dying in experimental animals. After Bruchanenko's death shortly before the war, Negovsky continued his experiments, and when the German army marched into the Soviet Union, he became a frontline physician— and happened to be in the hospital where Private Zderepanov met with violent death. With a cardiac massage, a number of stitches, and the rapid administration of an abundant supply of oxygen and blood, Negovsky succeeded in invalidating the death certificate. He went on to become the first medical specialist on death, leading a still-growing number of physicians in a field that rapidly became dominated by researchers in the Soviet Union. Negovsky's vocation and close association with death culminated a few years after the war in the founding of the now-famed Moscow Laboratory for the Resuscitation of the Organism.

Here death took on a new and more precise meaning. It was studied as a clinical event to be analyzed throughout all of its stages. The word "resuscitation" referred not to a miracle, but to a treatment now practiced in hundreds of centers in the Soviet Union and elsewhere in the world. In the last few years more than six thousand Soviet physicians have tried Negovsky's methods and several thousand people who "died" as a result of shock, loss of blood, heart attack, electrocution, and other accidents, have been resuscitated.

First experimenting with laboratory animals, Negovsky found a way to stimulate, in slow motion, the process of dying. This painless and "reversible" killing simply consists of bleeding an animal. A large loss of blood brings about a severe shock, a profound depression of organic functions, then a series of clear-cut features representing the "disturbance and extinction of the vital functions" which Negovsky calls "preterminal states."

These preterminal states are characterized by the slowing down and finally the arrest of respiration and heartbeat. If electrodes are attached to the animal's skull, bursts of excitation from the cerebral cortex (the outer portion of the brain, which constitutes the "higher centers" of the body's central nervous system) are observed, presumably reflecting the brain's attempts to stir all of the body's resources against death.

Then begins the next stage leading toward death:

agony or, rather, the agonal stage, for it usually follows unconsciousness and involves no pain. The functioning of the cerebral cortex is profoundly disturbed, notes Negovsky, and its regulating influence over the medulla stops (the medulla is the lowest, posterior part of the brain, an intermediary between the cortex and the rest of the central nervous system).

But even as the cortex gives out, resistance to death still goes on, carried on independently but erratically by the medulla and the spinal cord.

Respiration and heartbeat can return in a burst of energy as all the reserves of the nervous system still remaining in the medulla and the spinal cord are mobilized against death. Some basic reflexes are sporadically triggered, and blood is redistributed by spontaneous spasms of the vessels in the brain and the heart, in a last attempt to maintain the waning supply of oxygen to these organs. This clinical agony may last from a few minutes only, to several hours, depending on the cause of death, and the state of the organism.

Then, comes clinical death. It is, says Negovsky, "the final, but in many cases, still reversible, stage of dying." Heart activity and respiration have ceased. Consciousness has been lost usually much before this, but life at some low level is still present—an isolated, primitive life of individual tissues and organs.

One of these individual organs is the brain. As long as it survives, revival of the clinically dead organism may still be possible.

Experiments in Negovsky's Laboratory for the Resuscitation of the Organism (which stems directly from the Soviet Academy of Sciences) have shown that this reversible period of clinical death is normally limited to five, six, seldom more than eight minutes. The precise reasons for this limit are now known: In order to go on living, brain cells must be supplied with oxygen, which "burns" carbohydrates to supply the energy necessary to keep these cells alive. At the time of clinical death, the heart pumps no more blood to the brain. Thus deprived of oxygen, the brain still has an emergency supply of energy at its disposal: anaerobic glycolysis, another way of burning sugars and proteins, but in the absence of oxygen. This emergency supply is short, and becomes exhausted in a few minutes. Then, brain cells become permanently damaged. Even if some portions of the brain survive longer (those, for instance, needed to maintain the vegetative functions of the organism) other parts of the cortex are irreversibly destroyed. A man brought back to life after the reserves of anaerobic glycolysis have been exhausted may remain an imbecile for the rest of his life.

More recently, Negovsky has succeeded in prolonging clinical death by several hours. Inducing hypothermia, or low temperature, in an organism, causes a slowing down of its processes. When the brain or the entire organism is cooled down to a temperature of between 46° and 59° Farenheit, it survives but uses up its final reserves of energy so slowly that it can remain in the state of clinical death for several hours without suffering permanent damage. After resuscitation, all of the functions of the central nervous system can be reestablished.

Evidently the best time to revive a man is not during clinical death but before clinical death sets in, during the agonal state, when the physician can have much more than five or six minutes at his disposal. Agony, however, can be very brief, and when the doctors arrive, the patient may already be "clinically dead."

A standard method of "treating death" has been developed at Negovsky's laboratory. No way is known, he points out, to act directly upon the higher divisions of the brain, which have "died" last. Instead, one must work backward, first to restore the activity of the heart rapidly enough for it to feed blood into the brain, before the brain is damaged. Negovsky has found empirically that the best way to achieve this is to make a rapid transfusion of fully oxygenated blood into the arteries of the patient, toward the heart.

Usually, the safe method of making a standard transfusion is to let blood slowly flow into the *veins* of the patient. Blood is then normally integrated into the circulation, from the vein to the heart which pumps it into the lungs, where blood receives fresh oxygen to be distributed throughout the body.

During clinical death, this obviously wouldn't work, for the heart has stopped. Hence blood, already saturated with oxygen, must be pumped under pressure into the arteries, centripetally, that is, toward the heart. It then brings in oxygen and restores the coronary circulation in the vessels which crisscross the heart muscle. This revives the heart muscle which, in turn, starts pumping blood elsewhere, notably to the brain. This sequence of events is possible only because the heart muscle is so constituted as to contract spontaneously, going into action without receiving "orders" from the brain, which is still incapable of giving any. Respiration, on the other hand, is controlled by the brain, and will return only *after* the brain is revived.

The return of spontaneous respiration in fact indicates with some precision how much of the brain has started to function. If breathing can continue even when the patient is unconscious, when his cortex does not manifest itself, it is because the respiratory reflex is controlled by the medulla and goes on until the medulla itself gives out. Conversely, during resuscitation it is the medulla which assumes the first emergency cerebral function, as it did the last. The first spontaneous breath, therefore, indicates that the medulla has started functioning again. Artificial respiration during resuscitation is then necessary, not only to keep the lungs oxygenating the blood which is flowing through the body again, but also to trigger, by a sort of ricochet or reflex stimulation, the respiratory center in the medulla.

If the medulla does not start working five to ten minutes after clinical death, it is likely that the attempt to revive the body has failed, for the brain will be too damaged to resume normal functions. In such a case, even if resuscitation does succeed, the brain will not be normal: damaged cortical cells cannot regenerate and destroyed tissue is replaced by an inert scar.

In a few experiments, which Dr. Negovsky still cannot completely account for, animals were resuscitated without "brain freezing" after thirty to sixty minutes of clinical death, but such exceptions represent an infinitesimal percentage of his experience. (A similar, apparently unique case, also happened with a human patient, in Minsk, where a young man was brought back to life after forty-five minutes of clinical death, without suffering noticeable brain damage. In his case, however, blood was artificially pumped into his body, and his heart was massaged, probably supplying enough oxygen to the brain to keep it alive.)

Drugs can be used to help resuscitation, notes Negovsky, but during clinical death itself, stimulants should be avoided. Stimulants reaching a dying brain would have the effect of "whipping a starved horse." They increase oxygen demand by brain cells, and can accelerate the biological, final death of the brain.

Lev Landau had been in the "agonal state" practically from the moment of the accident. The main brain stem did not manifest its existence, as if its connections to the rest of the body had been suddenly switched off. Since the unconscious physicist had stopped breathing on his own, the medulla and spinal cord functioned only erratically, if at all. The biological functions of the organism had to be sustained by five lifelines implanted permanently into the body: one tube into the trachea, connected to the respirator and breathing air into the lungs; one to the stomach, supplying the body with water; one to the veinous system, introducing food that could be directly assimilated into the blood; and two for elimination.

If the heart went on beating ceaselessly for four days after the accident it was, says Grashchenkov, "because it was the exceptionally strong heart of a man who never smoked, hardly ever drank, a healthy heart without a gram of fat." Even when clinical death claimed the broken body, it was not because the heart was damaged, but because it gave under the onslaught of repeated trauma, as if it were tired and wanted to rest after an exhausting struggle.

But it could not be allowed to rest. Countless hands around Landau's bedside efficiently went through the well-rehearsed motions of "resuscitation of the clinically dead organism," in a silence interrupted only by the indifferent, rhythmical breathing of the artificial lung.

A thick needle at the end of a syringe full of blood was introduced into Landau's left forearm, penetrating into the radial artery. Two hands immediately appeared to connect the syringe to a tube. Two more hands held the container from which donor blood, saturated with oxygen, was forced into the artery by compressed air.

Immediately, a manometer showed the rising pressure of blood pushing its way toward the heart: more than 200 millimeters of mercury, nearly double the normal arterial pressure.

Another hand reached for a syringe of epinephrin, the most powerful known drug to stimulate the heart muscle and to increase blood pressure. Epinephrin was injected into the artery, rapidly reaching the heart. The hand of another physician, who held a stethoscope to Landau's chest, now signaled as the heart gave a beat, then another. Irregularly at first, then more and more steadily, blood was pumped into the starved organism. Small amounts of strophantin, a digitalis-type preparation to stimulate and strengthen the heart and the central nervous system, was now added to the inflow of fresh blood. The heart went on beating, and death retreated.

"He lives," Grashchenkov told the anxious physicists and physicians gathered in the hallway. "He lives"—the word was passed on by telephone to Landau's friends. "Clinical death repelled—he lives," read the report on a blackboard installed in the main hall of the Moscow Institute for Physical Problems.

For millions of Muscovites, this Thursday, January 11, was a day just like any other. The temperature was about ten degrees above zero, and light snow flurries sporadically fell on the city, as usual.

Izvestia carried the usual type of information: A delegation of farmers from the Altai was attending an agricultural meeting in Moscow. Bekeru, chief of a work-brigade at the *kolkhoz* "Land of the Soviet," had been awarded the Order of Lenin. Several other *kolkhozniks* received the Sickle and Hammer Gold Medal, and a few were elevated to the status of "heroes of socialist labor." Garbousov, the Soviet Minister of Finance, published a letter answering an earlier article criticizing illogical spending of national funds, and a brief news item mentioned a report from Washington that unemployment in the United States had grown by another 100,000, reaching a peak of 4,091,000. There was an article entitled "The Poor in Spirit," about Ludwig Erhard and West Germany; there were reports on the growth of trade between Great Britain and the Soviet Union, about friendship with Egypt, about Soviet plans to build a metallurgical factory in Baghdad, about Cosmonaut Titov's glorious visit to Bandung, and an article entitled, "We Are with You, People of Spain." A short item, headlined "For Sale: the Symbol of a City," noted that "In the cruel world of capitalistic business, everything can be bought and sold— land and forests, factories and ships, enormous buildings owned by millionaires, shacks for the poor, and even the labor force," and went on to mention the purchase of the Empire State Building by the Prudential Life Insurance Company. Nothing unusual.

Nowhere was there any mention of the drama that was being lived by a goodly portion of the city's intelligentsia, no announcement of the *avaria* on Dimitrovsky Chaussée. As usual, traffic accidents were ignored by the press.

But the news had started to spread through the Moscow grapevine. Rumor had it that Landau was near death, perhaps even dead. So many taxis had taken passengers to the Timiriasevsky District Hospital, far out toward the northern suburbs, that the drivers almost automatically addressed customers going there as "professor," and sometimes inquired about Dau's condition.

A new world had taken shape around Landau, a world whose people lost much of their interest in the world outside, and who only occasionally and half-heartedly made contact with it. "I couldn't help imagining it as a sort of biological cell, with ramifications spreading throughout the city upon which it fed," commented one of Dau's physicians.

Concordia Terentievna and Igor have returned from the country *dacha* to their apartment across the institute's courtyard. Cora sits by the telephone, alone, but it doesn't ring. Igor, a high-school student expected to graduate this year, crosses the courtyard into the institute where today his father should be holding his weekly seminar. On his way to collect books he left at the institute a week earlier, Igor passes the blackboard in front of which his father's students are gathered. They awkwardly look down and he awkwardly nods, too shy or too shaken to stop and look or to say anything. Igor bears a striking resemblance to his father—but only in the lower part of the face: the same large mouth, the prominent buck teeth that give his shy smile the same engaging frankness.

At the hospital, several physicians and a dozen physicists are on duty. Irochka, who has not left the hospital since Sunday, rests on a chair in a corner of the "physicists' headquarters." Once more, the telephone rings. "It's for you," someone says, and she wearily stands up to pick up the receiver. It is Boris calling, Irochka's fiancé, who has not seen her for nearly a week and has been trying to persuade her to leave the hospital, if only for a few hours.

"But, Boris, I've told you I can't, and I've asked you not

to call me here," she says, a note of irritation in her voice. "The telephone must be left free. I'll see you next week sometime." But the young man insists. "It's your father. He's ill." Irochka, pale, hangs up. "What is the matter?" asks one of the physicists, and she explains that her father is sick. "We'll drive you over," they offer, using the familiar *tyi*, the Russian for "thou," because she has become their friend.

Irochka goes down to one of the several Volgas waiting in the courtyard. It's a long drive to the center of the city. "I'll wait for you. Let me know how he is," says the physicist at the wheel as Irochka runs up the stairs to her small family apartment.

"Papa! I thought you were ill," she exclaims as her father opens the door—then she sees, behind him, Boris with downcast eyes, who starts to apologize. Pink with rage, she stalks towards him, her small fists tightened. "But, Irochka, I only wanted to see you and I thought . . ." —but his explanations are stopped short by a resounding slap delivered with all the force of a young woman's scorn. "*Svinya!*" she snaps. "You pig. I never want to see you again." In tears, Irochka kisses her astounded father, apologizes that she cannot stay, and runs down to the car waiting in the street.

Back at the hospital, the telephone keeps ringing. Now it is the Kharkov Physics-Technical Institute, where Landau once was the director, inquiring about his condition. Then it's a laboratory in Leningrad, in Alma Ata, in Erevan. From Minsk in White Russia to the remotest laboratory in Far-Eastern Siberia, Dau's former students and his friends want to know.

Night falls, and still Dau lives. Aliosha Abrikossov, on

the night shift, spreads his notebooks on a desk, next to Vladimir Sudakov, the driver on that fateful Sunday trip.

During the night, in her apartment next to the institute, Cora wakes up time and again, dreaming that the telephone is ringing. Her heart beating fast, almost painfully, she picks it up, but only the buzz of an empty line breaks the silence, deepened by the soft, endless *mitiel*, the dry, crisp snow flurries that give Moscow a lunar beauty at night under the Kremlin's eerie red stars, before the white carpet is swept away by the well-ordered ranks of rumbling, heavy snow-removal machinery.

In the morning of January 12, Landau is still living. Sdenek Kunz, well-known Czech neurosurgeon who has flown to Moscow at the request of Landau's physicians, sadly looks on the scientist's motionless body. As a conclusion to his examination, Kunz has written: "The trauma sustained are incompatible with life." Now he speaks, as if to himself. "It is impossible. He cannot live. I cannot understand how he has survived so long. Still . . ." But he sees that the doctors, the physicists around him will not give up hope, and he wonders at the feat accomplished by the devotion of so many men. . . . "But one thing you must remember," adds Professor Kunz. "If he survives, you must, as soon as possible, you *must* stop feeding him intravenously. This is inadequate support, an invitation to almost inevitable autointoxication of the body. It can never be carried on for any length of time." Then Professor Kunz apologizes for leaving—he must return to his patients in Prague.

Another bedside conference takes place over the unconscious scientist. The physicians realize that it is out of the question yet to feed Landau through the stomach, which is still completely blocked. They cannot but conclude,

"We'll have to do our best this way." The duration of the intravenous feeding of the totally unconscious, unresponsive body has already exceeded any in their previous experience, and the irrevocable autointoxication predicted by Kunz and feared by all slowly sets in. Blood tests are made every two or three hours, determining the wavering proportions of proteins and electrolytes, the disproportions of alkalinity and acidity, the accumulation of cellular debris. The preparations introduced into the veins are constantly altered to correct the imbalance. Constantly, the breathing rate of the respirator and the regulation of oxygen content introduced into Landau's lungs must be adjusted. Water still accumulates in the body, causing it to swell. Traumatic paralysis of the bowels persists. On January 14, seven days after the accident, hypostatic pneumonia sets in—a general inflammation of the lungs, brought about by the persistent irritation from injuries and infection, by the immobility of the body in the prone position on its back. Both bronchi—the windpipes leading from the trachea to the lungs—are clogged up with mucus. Drains must be introduced to clear passages for air, but it seems to be too late. Once more, clinical death set in.

Once again, it was repelled, and again on January 16, and on January 18, death returned to claim the body it was entitled to—each time to be fought off from the tight, stubborn world of doctors, nurses, and physicists around Landau.

Almost two weeks had passed since the accident. Landau was alive, but still unconscious. Shortly before his fifty-fourth birthday on January 22, another swelling of the brain began, and urea was injected to treat it. Now, an excess of urea in the body blocked the kidneys that were no longer able to eliminate the body's waste products. A new kind of poisoning had started: uremia, the dangerous accumulation in the blood and in the body of residual nitrogen compounds. The body took on the sickly smell of urine. Once more, the specialists who were needed gathered at the bedside. Urologists were ready to perform the analysis that enabled them to determine the best treatment, to prepare the required injections. Slowly, the kidneys returned to normal function, discharging the accumulation of waste products. For the first time since the accident, the skin took on a healthier, almost pink color. Landau's friends rejoiced, but Cora was not in Moscow to see her husband: on the verge of a nervous breakdown, she had been taken to a rest clinic near the city.

Bedside consultations between medical specialists were still held twice, three times a day. Danger lurked from so many sides that each specialist consulted others, planning a strategy to make sure that the side effects of one treatment would not bring about complications elsewhere. Jaundice set in, and was rapidly treated. Orthopedists were helpless, for there was no way of treating bone injuries in the classical manner: the patient could barely be moved and could not be turned over, prohibiting the use of casts or tension. The physicists constructed a special bed for Landau, an intricate contraption using pullies, cranks, and pneumatic cushions to permit some movement of the patient, but the bones could be rejoined only approximately, and some of the hip bones were healing off of their normal position, resulting in the shortening of Landau's left leg by nearly two inches.

Stomach and bowel function slowly returned and at long last, intravenous feeding was discontinued. Food could now be introduced through a thin plastic tube entering the nose, descending down the esophagus and into the stomach. Professor Menshikov and other dietitians conferred with the medical team to determine the most adequate list of menus. All the carefully selected foods had to be measured, crushed, and mixed into a uniform paste, sufficiently liquid to be poured down the tube. This strange type of cooking became the responsibility of a physicist, Professor Alexander Shalnikov, a corresponding member of the Academy of Sciences, and of his wife. Their concoctions were carefully measured out into milk bottles and delivered every day to the hospital. "Even the best caviar," remembers Shalnikov, "had to be crushed into a sort of dark, horrible looking liquid paste."

Physicists took the responsibility of providing the Shalnikovs with any type of food that might be recommended for Landau. They bought whatever could be bought in Moscow—but some of the ingredients were not so easily available. Fruit, for instance, can be scarce and bitter during Moscow winters; the physicists drove again to Moscow airports, to buttonhole Aeroflot pilots on outgoing flights. "Flying to Egypt? Good! Here is what we need," they said, giving the pilot a list and explaining their purpose. And in flew the freshest oranges and grapefruits and dates to be seen in Moscow, delivered by young physicists proud to be contributing their share to Landau's new life. From the Crimea, there came the luscious large grapes grown in sunny hothouses. From the Black Sea, fresh fish and caviar in glass jars, and crabs from the Baltic—delicacies none of which the still unconscious Landau could taste or eat—to be macerated and crushed, bringing new life into his body, a fresh, healthy, rosy tint to his skin.

"From the therapeutic viewpoint," says Professor Alim

Damir, "the worst was over in the middle of February, some five weeks after the accident. Fractures were almost mended, and superficial injuries had vanished, replaced by well-healed scars. Infections had disappeared. Both lungs were healed, in spite of the tremendous trauma they had received. Digestion was perfect. The kidneys worked, and the heart beat regularly."

Landau, however, was still completely unconscious. His eyes were glassy, fixed, saying nothing and seeing nothing. "When you looked at him," Maya Bessarab, Landau's niece, remembers, "his eyes seemed to look through you into eternity."

Neither flashes of light in front of his eyes, nor noise near his ears, elicited the slightest reaction on his part. He did not even have the most elementary pain reflexes, whether pinched, or pricked with a needle, or even when his bones had been set into place without any form of anesthesia. Even the breathing reflex did not start again. If the respirator was disconnected, Landau's chest would rise and fall only for a few seconds, then stop.

Neurological and neurosurgical specialists, under the leadership of Grashchenkov and of the veteran Professor Boris Yegorov, director of the Moscow Neurosurgical Institute, were at a loss. Why did the brain refuse to function? They had no previous experience to draw on, no case histories to consult: They did not know of a single patient who suffered such massive trauma and recovered to create a precedent.

Time and again they rehashed the same questions, examining the sparse evidence. Was there under the skull a large blood clot that had not been detected during the exploratory craniotomy performed on the night after the accident? If so, did it press upon neighboring tissues, preventing recovery, perhaps even inflicting further damage by squeezing capillary arteries of the brain, depriving more cells of oxygen, and destroying them. Or was there, instead, a number of small hemorrhages, which were likely to dissolve by themselves? Was the brain only "frozen" in anabiosis, a suspended animation from which it would slowly come awake?

If a single, large center of disturbance in the form of a hematoma existed in the brain, the risk of an operation should be taken because the surgical removal of the swelling might immediately restore cerebral function. Small hemorrhages, however, should not be operated, for the harm caused by several operations in the brain would be greater than the good.

The physicians did not know the reason for the brain's prolonged inactivity, and could not agree on the course to be followed. They agreed, however, that Landau's body had recovered sufficiently so that if anything at all was to be done, it should be done now.

Had the patient been anyone else, a decision would have been taken rapidly, probably to operate if only to explore the damaged area. But the patient was Landau, one of the Soviet Union's most important, perhaps its most brilliant scientist. Someone would have to take the responsibility to operate, to risk damage to his brain by surgery which might turn out not to be warranted. In a normal brain, the result of a slight surgical damage often goes unnoticed—but in Landau's, it might make the difference between genius and only normal intelligence.

Day after day the physicists who were his friends leaned over Dau's unconscious body, tried to talk to him, hoping to see in his eyes the spark of life that would mean the brain was awakening. But there was none. They grew restless, endlessly harrassing the medical team. They feared that the doctors were too conservative, that they hesitated too long to make a move that would engage their responsibility.

Toward the end of February, Kapitza and Lifshitz decided to act. If the physicists had succeeded in spurring the best Soviet specialists to save Landau's life, couldn't they now repeat the same on a worldwide scale to save his mind?

Surely, they felt, there were in the world neurologists or neurosurgeons whose advice could now be valuable, who could bring in a fresh viewpoint. In conversations with Yegorov and Grashchenkov, Kapitza learned the names of some of these men. "Let us ask them to come," Kapitza told Mstislav Keldysh, the president of the Soviet Academy of Sciences. Keldysh agreed and contacted Leonid Brezhnev, head of the Supreme Soviet, then the nominal president of the Soviet Union, asking him that every facility be offered the foreign scientists to reach Moscow as rapidly as possible. Brezhnev agreed, and made a few brief but significant telephone calls.

Soviet embassies in Canada and in France were notified to contact the selected consultants, and to arrange for a prompt and comfortable trip to Moscow. The usually time-consuming visa requirements were to be completely ignored, no matter where the scientist came from. The question was—would the specialists consent to leave their own hospitals or clinics, to travel thousands of miles, to help a man they might never have heard of before?

On Saturday, February 24, the telephone rang at the home of Professor Wilder G. Penfield, outstanding Canadian neurologist, founder of the Montreal Neurological Institute. It rang in Paris, in the homes of neurosurgeon

Gerard Guillot, and neurologist Raymond Garçin. A voice with a noticeable Russian accent announced that the call came from the Soviet Embassy, and made the unexpected suggestion of a trip to Moscow "as soon as possible—today or tomorrow" to act as consultants in the treatment of a patient recovering from a traffic accident. The patient was one Lev Landau, "an important Soviet physicist."

CHAPTER 10

International
Brain Trust

(MARCH 1962)

ON FEBRUARY 20, a nurse who gave Landau an injection had the impression that he cringed, ever so slightly, when the needle was introduced into his arm. But physicians, who watched carefully when the next injection was given, saw no reaction at all.

A few of the visitors at the hospital believed that they noticed "something new" in Landau's eyes. On February 22, the physicist's niece, Maya Bessarab, wrote in her diary:

I saw for the first time an intelligent look in Dau's eyes. The eyes were different, as if they recovered their capacity for seeing. I was speaking to him softly, telling him that he was recovering and that all the terrible things had passed. He listened with his eyes riveted to me, and he stopped listening as soon as I stopped talking. But as long as I talked, his eyes never left me.

Such brief glimpses of consciousness, however, were still exceptional and unpredictable. Physicians had not observed any, and when they prepared for the "international medical concilium" suggested by Kapitza and Lifshitz, they still attributed such impressions as Maya's to wishful thinking.

Five thousand miles from Moscow, Professor Wilder Penfield had never heard of Landau, let alone of the drama that had been taking place in a hospital on the outskirts of Moscow. The telephone call from the Soviet Embassy came on February 24, a Saturday afternoon, shortly after Penfield returned home from the Montreal Neurological Institute.

When the embassy official outlined the amazing history of the patient and explained who the man was, the Canadian neurologist became concerned with the possibility that his presence might be requested by the Soviet government, rather than by the medical specialists who were treating Landau. "I shall come, but only if this request is made by the neurologists treating the patient," said Penfield, hoping to avoid the embarrassing situation of his being forced upon his Russian colleagues by their government officials. "Very well," answered the Soviet Diplomat. "We shall call you back shortly."

Penfield's answer was immediately cabled to the Ministry of Foreign Affairs in Moscow and transmitted to the physicists' headquarters at the Timiriasevsky District Hospital, where Yevgheni Lifshitz picked up the "emergency telephone."

"Would you please put me through to Professor Penfield in Montreal right away," he told the well-trained operator, who wouldn't have shown much surprise by now if she had been asked to call the White House. A few minutes later Penfield was on the line. Lifshitz explained that Penfield's presence as a consultant was indeed requested by the medical team that was about to make an important decision. "Who suggested that I come?" asked Penfield. "Professors Yegorov and Grashchenkov," answered Lifshitz. "Please wait a few seconds. They would like to talk to you."

Another voice now spoke from Moscow. Penfield recognized Yegorov, the veteran neurosurgeon whose institute he had visited several times; then Grashchenkov, whom Penfield had met more than twenty years earlier, when Grashchenkov had visited the Montreal Neurological Institute. Penfield no longer hesitated. "Of course, my friends, of course, I'll come. I'll take the next plane out."

On the following day, instead of leaving on a skiing trip he had planned with his wife, Penfield boarded a plane for the long journey east.

When he landed at Moscow's Sheremetevo Airport in the evening of February 26, Grashchenkov was waiting for him. During the forty-five-minute-long drive from the airport the Soviet physician gave Landau's case history in detail, concluding: "Today, it has been almost seven weeks. And still, no sign of consciousness, no sign of awakening cerebral function."

Penfield was deep in thought. Leaving aside the enormous physical trauma described by Grashchenkov and the extremely long period of unconsciousness, the case did not seem to be entirely without precedent. Penfield himself had operated on a number of patients, usually victims of traffic accidents, who had been completely unconscious for several days because of an injury to the brain, an injury which frequently resulted in the formation of a hematoma. Sometimes surgery could lead to a dramatic recovery. At any rate, Penfield felt that the risk from an operation that was almost considered routine at his institute, was small.

Without stopping for dinner or to check into a hotel, Penfield was driven to examine the patient. "Physicists and physicians seemed to be everywhere in the hospital," remembers the Canadian neurologist. "Lifshitz, wearing a white hospital gown, met me in the hall and introduced himself. Yegorov was there, and many physicians whom I did not know. As we walked toward Landau's room, I was moved by the concern expressed on so many faces, by the warmth of their greeting."

Night had fallen over the city when Penfield made a first, brief examination, noting that "The patient's apparently total lack of reaction to any stimulus seemed to evidence complete unconsciousness, complete isolation of the brain stem from the rest of the organism. The clinical picture, the X-ray photograph of the skull, suggested the presence of a hematoma or some other trauma acting on the brain."

"If Landau were my father, I would operate," he told his Soviet colleagues, but he found them so hesitant and conservative that he wondered whether Landau's reputation and the importance given to the case had not made them shy away from the same conclusion.

"But what if there is no hematoma?" wondered Professor Yegorov. "Shouldn't he be left alone, slowly to recover by himself? What of the trauma, the shock of an operation in his condition?" Penfield reiterated his view that the risk of the operation was of no consequence. In recent years, brain surgery had been perfected to such a degree that surgical damage was unlikely. "There should be no shock," he told Yegorov, "if the operation is performed by Yegorov himself."

It was late, and Penfield looked weary. "There will be time to decide tomorrow," said Yegorov, realizing how tired the Canadian must be after the long journey to Moscow.

On the following morning, February 27, the first full-scale international concilium met at Landau's bedside. In addition to the Soviet specialists, it included Wilder Penfield of Canada, Gerard Guillot and Raymond Garçin who had just arrived from Paris, and Sdenek Kunz, who had been asked, once more, to fly in from Prague.

On the same morning, Landau's wife Cora left the clinic to which she had been taken, near hysteria, not long after the accident. She asked to be driven directly to the Timiriasevsky District Hospital.

As she neared the hospital she could see only through a veil of tears. "There was a long walk through a hall," she remembers. "I heard that foreign brain specialists were with Dau. Nobody seemed to notice me, and I felt like a stranger, unknown to the crowd of doctors assembled around my husband. Only a few of Dau's students recognized me."

Physicians were crowding Dau's room and Cora leaned against the doorway, her heart beating fast, afraid to walk in, afraid to disturb the specialists who were talking about her husband, afraid even to look. She listened, grasping a word here and there. She understood only little English, and most of the exchanges were taking place in that language. She heard a few words in Russian, mentioning surgery, brain damage, the need to transfer her husband to the Moscow Neurosurgical Institute.

A few minutes after she arrived, the group of specialists

walked out to continue their conference in an adjoining room. None of them noticed or recognized her, and Cora entered the small room.

. Two nurses stood by Dau's bedside. "When I saw him, I felt that everything would be all right. His skin no longer had this terrifying appearance of the first day, the dry, dark yellow parchment that did not seem to belong on a living man. It was pink, living, healthy.

"When I leaned over him, I saw life in his eyes. I believe he recognized me right away. But then, I remembered that the doctors spoke of complete unconsciousness, of the need for brain surgery, and I was frightened. Don't they know he is conscious? I wondered."

Hesitantly, gently, Cora started talking to her husband who, it seemed to her, had returned from the dead. She held his face between her hands. She talked to him and he looked at her; he did not smile or make any sign of recognition, but she felt that he understood. "Dau, Dauchka, I know you cannot talk, you have no strength," she said. "But you recognize me. If you hear me, if you have recognized me, please make a sign, close your eyes, or nod your head."

Slowly, Landau closed his eyes.

Cora felt faint and terribly afraid, afraid of the operation. The words she had heard so clearly came back. "Deep brain surgery . . . deep brain surgery." Would Dau survive? Even if he recovered from deep brain surgery, would he still be himself, would he be the person she loved and knew so well? Cora could not help remembering the stories she had heard about the possibility of complete change of personality after brain surgery.

Again, she asked him, "Dau, if you hear me, if you recognize me, please close your eyes, nod your head." Dau

closed and opened his eyes several times. Poor, wonderful
Dauchka, she thought. He can understand, he wants to
answer, but he cannot.

The nurses saw her stand up, tears in her eyes. What
should she do? "I was afraid to tell this to the doctors.
They knew too well I was such an emotional person, and
now I was so upset again, almost hysterical. They would
not listen to me!"

As she stood there, the international concilium went on
next door. The French specialists, Guillot and Garçin,
had been astounded at Landau's clinical history. "We do
not understand how he could survive. Patients with such
injuries die," they declared. "We are amazed at the persis-
tency, courage, and skill of our Russian colleagues who
have wrested the patient from the clutches of death," they
wrote later in a joint conclusion to their visit. "We can
neither change nor add anything to what the Russian colleagues have done. . . . The first stage of the fight for life is
successfully completed."

The Russian neurologists still insisted that there should
be no surgery, but Penfield held a different view. "My
impression was that the lesion must be just above the
midbrain, in the vicinity of the corpus striatum, perhaps
on both sides of the brain. I was in favor of ventriculog-
raphy, but found a great deal of timidity on the part of
the Russians," he wrote in his clinical report. Ventric-
ulography, the radiographic examination of cerebral circulation, might pinpoint the lesion, but it would require
the injection of an opaque substance into the blood system, and movement of the patient, which Soviet physicians wanted to avoid.

"I would like to see the patient again, alone," said Penfield, suggesting that the conference resume after lunch.

He made his way through a group of physicists in the hall, but Professors Guillot and Garçin were surrounded by so many that they could not move. It was Wednesday, the day of Kapitza's seminar at the Physics Institute, but most of Landau's students were at the hospital—and the French specialists happened to be the sources of the latest information. "They may be Frenchmen, but lunch will have to wait," remarked one of the students, as Guillot and Garçin started answering a barrage of questions.

Penfield now sat at Dau's bedside. Two nurses stood quietly behind him. Cora, her face streaked with dried tears, saw the foreign specialist who had been pointed out to her earlier, the man who wanted her husband to be operated on.

She came to him and haltingly tried to explain that Dau had recognized her. One of the nurses mentioned in English that Concordia Terentievna was Landau's wife, but Penfield did not understand what Cora said. Then, she went to her husband again.

"Dau, please, if you recognize me, close your eyes," she pleaded. As he had done a few minutes earlier, Landau closed his eyes. Penfield watched, motionless. Again, Cora repeated her plea, and again, Landau closed his eyes, opened them, closed them again, obviously in reply to his wife. Several Russain physicists were entering the room. A nurse held them off, whispering, "Wait. . . . Look."

Penfield now leaned over, started talking to Landau in English. "Perhaps we should translate into Russian," suggested one of the physicians. "Don't bother. It's easier in English," said Penfield, who had been told that Landau was fluent in that language, as well as in French and in German. And he went on, "Professor Landau, if you recognize your wife, please close your eyes or nod." Four times he repeated his request, and four times Landau closed his eyes, even seemed to make an effort to move his head, his consciousness and his energy spurred by the presence of his wife, who had become a new stimulus in the now too familiar surroundings of the hospital. The tension in the room had been such that one could hear, now, the release of breaths that had been held silent. "My God!" said someone. "Dau saw! He understood!"

"Landau's eyes had noticeably shifted from myself to his wife, and then, back to me again," said Penfield later. "When I moved my head to the right and then to the left, his eyes followed me. This was the first manifestation of consciousness I had seen in this patient. It was evident that consciousness was returning."

It was, also, the reward doctors and physicists alike had been hoping for during fifty days of relentless care over an apparently lifeless body.

Just how many people had a share in the recovery of a man dead four times will never be known, nor will it be remembered just how much time and energy had been given so freely, either at Landau's bedside, or waiting near telephones or in airports or behind the wheel of a car, in the performance of the countless, often menial, tasks that were necessary to provide Dau with the most complete nursing care, where every need had been foreseen and an answer prepared and rehearsed so that it could be given with the utmost precision and timeliness.

The personal sacrifices willingly and often anonymously made by so many are a rare example of collective enthusiasm that was nothing short of a social phenomenon. No task was too humble, nor too great, not to be undertaken by those who loved and admired Landau and who communicated their devotion to so many others. Between the people who made possible what became known as "The Miracle of Moscow," there was born a rare feeling of closeness. From one day to the next, friendships came to exist between complete strangers, between people who discovered in their neighbors human qualities they often hadn't suspected existed at all.

The devotion of so many had an irresistible impact also on geographical or political or ideological frontiers with which men have divided the world. It was, as one physicist put it, "As if a great number of people had been struck by a natural catastrophe, which helped demolish man-made barriers standing between people, which reduced mountains that separate them into the molehills they should be. Friendship, respect, admiration were born, that have left a timeless mark in many hearts."

Will the physicists ever forget Irochka, the simple, young girl who took a full share of their task, placing her new duty above the concerns of her private life? Will Kapitza forget Penfield, and Penfield, Kapitza? After the decision was taken not to operate, Kapitza met at his home with a small group of friends, whom he told of his admiration for the Canadian neurologist. "It takes a great scientist and a great man," said Kapitza, "to admit willingly that he was wrong the day before." Likewise, later remarked a physician, it took a great scientist and a great man, like Kapitza, to make such a comment. A lesser person might have been critical, not realizing that Penfield's impression was fully justified by the clinical evidence, not realizing also that errors committed are innumerably more frequent that errors willingly recognized.

In the atheistic society of Soviet scientists, a small part of credit was even granted to God—a courtesy, perhaps, to those Western colleagues who believed in Him. It was a Muscovite physicist who commented, "Landau's life was saved thirty-three percent thanks to the doctors, thirty-three percent thanks to the physicists, thirty-three percent thanks to the strength of his own body, and one percent thanks to God." And a physician who replied, "Hope for God if you will, but don't make mistakes."

For the first time in many weeks, Cora knew deep inside that her husband was alive again, that he was himself. Dau's son Igor, when he now passed by the blackboard in the hall of the Institute of Physical Problems, no longer cringed but looked to read the latest report on his father's recovery. Physically, Landau had passed a point of no return. The collective optimism that greeted his first glimpse of consciousness was written on the faces of his friends. And none of them seemed to realize, in those few days after the foreign consultants returned home, that such optimism was, perhaps, premature.

For would Landau's brain now recover its memory, its exceptional reasoning power? Would he ever again understand anything about physics? Would he ever return to work? Or to any semblance of a normal life?

In spite of spectacular progress in recent years in the understanding of neurophysiological processes, the most fundamental notions about brain function are still lacking. Penfield once wrote:

In this era of discovery there is an atmosphere of false expectation. The false expectation is that science will soon solve all problems. Science will do the impossible. Uneasy philosophers seem to be calling downward through the clouds: "What Ho, Science! Any new evidence to publish on the translation of nerve impulse into thought, and thought into nerve impulse? Can you prove yet that there is no such translation, that consciousness and nervous activity are one and the same thing?"

The reply from below is silence, or at least it should be, complete silence. Any scientist who looks up from his work to declare, for example, that the truth is to be found in monism (the doctrine that mind and matter are one) or dualism (which separates the two), or that there is some middle ground, ceases to speak as a scientist. He may, for himself, believe that "man is a senseless cog in a blind machine." He may be a materialist. If so, that is his philosophical assumption. He may believe in dualism and may go, beyond that, to belief in the spirit of God and to dependence upon that spirit. But that is an act of faith. In either case he has done no more than to choose his religion.

However misty the attempts to connect nerve cells and the process of thought, a great number of facts have been established that can serve to build a working hypothesis, and lead to valid clinical results. It is clear, for instance, that function within the normal brain is achieved, in the words of the great physiologist Sir Charles Sherrington, by "transient electrical potentials traveling the fibers of the nervous system." But before planned voluntary action is possible, says Penfield:

There must occur within the brain a complicated re-direction of the entering potentials. The streams of sensory information must be arranged and organized. And to this organization must be added information from the individual's own past experience, pertinent data from the memory store-house of the brain. It is the organizing activity that comes between sensory input and voluntary motor output that consti-tutes the physical basis of the mind.

The mechanism of this organizing activity may be far from crystal-clear, but many of its elements have been identified.

The brain's sixteen billion or so cells, says Professor

Nikolai Grashchenkov, are known to be extremely sensitive to any change. The alterations in the endless flow of nervous impulses along the countless crisscrossing channels of information are reflected in the changes of electrical potentials in the brain, and can be studied with the help of electroencephalography, the recording of these potentials through electrodes applied to the skull.

The pathways of nerve impulses are known to form a very sensitive "feedback system" identified only in recent years, a feedback system similar to others that have been found to exist throughout the body and which are taking increasing importance in the understanding of life processes.

Just what is a feedback system? Probably the first, and one of the simplest man-made feedback systems, was designed by James Watt, of steam engine fame, to provide an automatic control mechanism to regulate the speed of his engine and to prevent it from blowing up from excessive steam pressure. This regulator consisted of a rod, which turned with the engine. Atop of the rod Watt attached two hinged moveable arms with heavy metal balls. When the engine turned, so did the rods, and the faster it turned, the more the steel balls were pulled away from the rod by centrifugal force. The arms which supported the steel balls were connected to the throttle valve in such a way that the faster the engine turned, the more the throttle valve was narrowed, the less steam was admitted, slowing the engine down. When the engine slowed down, the metal balls fell closer to their supporting rod, and the throttle valve opened up, increasing engine speed. The engine, in fact, regulated itself, but according to the design of its constructor.

The brain has an infinitely more complex, but similar in

principle, feedback organization involving electrical potentials instead of steam and rods. It also has "servo-
mechanisms" enabling great effects to be obtained from
an originally small impulse—mechanisms working much
in the fashion of power brakes or power steering. Both
feedback and servo-mechanisms play vital roles in the
functioning of the brain, the main generator of "nervous
energy" in the body.

The main seat both of servo-mechanisms and feedback
control in the brain seems to be the reticular formation
(*formatio reticularis*), a group of nerve fibers running
approximately through the center of the medulla, from
the spinal cord to the cortex itself. This is a logical position, for it is between the cortex and the spinal cord,
which passes on impulses back and forth between the
body and the main brain stem, that control must be exerted. There seem to be nervous connections radiating
from the reticular formation "as spokes radiate from the
hub of a wheel to its peripheral working rim," in the
words of the well-known neuroanatomist Horace W.
Magoun of the University of California. Groups of fibers
which transmit electrical impulses from the reticular formation to the surrounding areas are the efferent fibers,
and those leading information to the reticular formation
both from the body and from the cortex, afferent ones.

When the master control board of the reticular formation receives excitation in the form of nervous impulses, it
does not necessarily transmit the same impulses onward to
the cortex or to the body. Instead, if the excitation it receives is, for example, too violent, the reticular formation
builds up a block so that no information any longer passes
from the spinal cord to the cortex. If a complete block is
not necessary, the reticular formation becomes a sort of

sieve, filtering through only part of the impulses and directing them to the appropriate receiving area.

On the contrary, when minute excitation needs to be amplified, the reticular formation can supply its own energy, acting not as a barrier or as a sieve, but as a source of power. It acts in the manner of a radio amplifier that raises low energy waves to the higher energy level of sound. Quoting Professor Magoun's more scientific terminology: "Stimulation of different regions of the reticular formation can evoke powerful inhibition of facilitation of a wide range of motor performances including flexor and extensor reflexes, decerebrate rigidity, and cortical motor response." Flexor and extensor muscles, for instance, can be triggered by the reticular formation or by some other part of the central nervous system in the form of reflexes: if you accidentally place a hand on a hot stove, you will withdraw it before you even feel the pain—which will be felt via the cortex fractions of a second later.

The reticular formation and the existence of its inhibitory role were discovered more than a hundred years ago, but not until recent years has the paramount importance of its feedback and servo-mechanisms been grasped. It is now clear that the reticular formation, long believed to be a mere pathway, a messenger faithfully delivering impulses from the body to the brain and back, plays the much more important role of regulator—distributing, amplifying, decreasing, or completely cutting off these impulses. Some of the inhibitory or facilitatory areas of the reticular formation have even been pinpointed, in experimental animals at least, but it must not be believed that the reticular formation is all-powerful: it itself belongs to a feedback system, and is controlled not only by impulses received from the body via the spinal cord, but also by impulses coming from the cortex.

Let us again assume that a person suffers a relatively slight trauma to a limb. Without resorting to the higher levels of the brain, the reticular formation can trigger a reflex whereby the limb will be "automatically" withdrawn from the source of the trauma. The sensation of pain reaches consciousness only after the reflex has been provoked, and only then does the victim curse or react in some other conscious manner that may be regarded as a "high-level" cortical reaction.

In extreme cases, when the pain would be "unbearable," the feedback system cannot cope with it. At the onslaught of pain impulses from the body, the reticular formation receives some sort of a message from the cortex, telling it, in effect, that "this pain is too much to bear." The reticular formation then completely blocks the "pain" impulse before it reaches consciousness, and pain is not felt (rather, where pain should be felt, none exists.)

These extreme cases, though relatively rare, do occur. The classical example, for instance, is that of a soldier's losing an arm on the battlefield, not feeling the loss, and going forward until he collapses from loss of blood. Another, which happened in New York a few years ago, was the case of the automobile driver whose left arm was torn off by a truck going in the opposite direction; he continued to drive until stopped by horrified onlookers who rushed him to the hospital.

The reticular formation, then, plays the key role in the onset of the so-called "state of shock," a state in which Landau had been deeply plunged for nearly two months, probably because he suffered trauma that was "too much" and never reached his consciousness. His brain was sundered from the outside world.

In addition, it was not unlikely that Landau's centrencephalic system was damaged. The centrencephalic system, a term coined by Penfield in 1952, represents the link between the two hemispheres of the higher brain— not a separate block of the brain, but a specific set of pathways projecting from areas of the sensory cortex into a central "information integrating area."

The problem for the neurologists was to determine the type and the location of damage, in order to determine a treatment—if any could be useful. Such a diagnosis can be attempted even if the brain does not functionally manifest itself, as the reasons for its inactivity can be hinted at by electroencephalography. Such recordings of electrical potentials in Landau's brain were made regularly, through a dozen electrodes taped to his skull.

Current from the normal brain, notes Professor Grashchenkov, comes in eight to twelve pulses per second, registering as a wave with an amplitude of 50 microvolts— the alpha wave. A few days after the accident, when the first recording was made, Landau's cerebral biocurrents presented an entirely different picture: They were irregular, its slow pulsations coming at the rate of three to four per second, with an amplitude varying between 200 and 250 microvolts. This pattern, known as the delta waves, continued as long as he was completely unconscious, confirming that the "sieve" of the reticular formation, normally filtering ingoing and outgoing information, was blocked. The delta rhythm is typical when no information reaches the brain, says Grashchenkov. Impulses come only from the brain cells themselves, indicating they are isolated—but not dead. At first, delta rhythm was picked up in every region of Landau's brain, showing up on the tracings from electrodes applied to any portion of his shaven head.

Then, when glimpses of consciousness started returning, another pattern arose in several regions: the theta rhythm, consisting of waves pulsating 16 to 20 times per second, with an amplitude of approximately 75 micro-volts. It indicated that some information had started going through, but chaotically.

This mixed pattern appeared at the beginning of March, after the international concilium recognized that consciousness had slowly started to return. Landau was then transferred to the Burdenko Neurosurgical Institute directed by Professor Boris Yegorov.

The ancient palace on Tverskaya-Yaniskaya Street is the heart of Soviet neurosurgery, where patients are usu-ally admitted only with a view to an operation. A dozen cases are operated on in an average day, under the direc-tion of Yegorov himself, with the diagnostic assistance of a staff under neurologist Mikhail Rappaport, and neuro-physiologist Yevgheni Rusinov, a specialist in electro-encephalography.

At that time the normal alpha rhythm still had not re-turned to any region of Landau's brain. It seemed that the brain not only had been isolated by the onslaught of im-pulses from his broken body, but also that it had received a blow severe enough to cause more extensive damage that was not identified, Grashchenkov believed. The re-turn of some cerebral function indicated that this damage was at least partly reversible and did not consist entirely of the destruction of cells, which do not regenerate but form an inert scar. The damage, Grashchenkov believed, consisted rather in the disconnection between cells, which can be repaired with time. The blow to the head must have been too strong to be buffered by the cerebrospinal fluid in the skull, which can absorb smaller shocks. "In-stead, the fluid must have been so compressed that it exploded, so to speak, within the various passages of the brain. This broke contact between a number of cells, blocking impulse pathways."

Grashchenkov himself had made a detailed hypothesis several years earlier of how this disconnection could take place: Normally, impulses from one nerve cell to the next pass through synapses (or synaptic junctions), the anatomical relay from one nerve cell to another. Rootlike ramifications of the cells are connected at these junctions by a sort of "button snap" which becomes chemically blocked during a severe shock. If the brain is not otherwise severely damaged, synapses can begin to function again.

In the case of Landau there was no way of knowing how much of the damage was permanent, how much was reversible. The worst could be feared: for a whole month after his transfer to the Burdenko Neurological Institute, his reflexes had been primitive only, consisting mainly of shrinking when he felt sudden pain. His manifestations of active, conscious thought, of awareness and of recognition, had been rare. By the end of March he still had not uttered a single word, though he could breathe on his own for as long as ten to fifteen minutes at a time when the respirator was discontinued. The surge of optimism a month earlier had proven to be premature. "We had helped save his life," said one of his students. "Would we regret this, if he never recovered his mind?"

CHAPTER 11

"I have become
rather queer . . ."

(APRIL–OCTOBER 1962)

ON SUNDAY, April 8, 1962, Landau spoke his first word in almost exactly three months.

For the past month Cora had visited him almost daily at the Burdenko Neurosurgical Institute, talked to him, asked questions. But if Dau reacted at all, it was only by closing his eyes, sometimes weakly nodding his head. He cringed at pain, tried to shrink away from an injection, and sometimes, fear was expressed on his face at the arrival of those physicians he had come to associate with pain. But the hope that the recovery of speech, intelligence, and memory would rapidly follow that of consciousness and of the most primitive reflexes had not been realized. Physicians and physicists alike started wondering again whether an operation would be the wisest course.

On that Sunday morning a nurse gave Dau a drink of

water from a rubber-nippled bottle. As she had done many times before, she asked him whether he'd had enough. Landau nodded.

"Now, shouldn't you say 'thank you'?" she asked with a smile, slowly repeating several times the Russian word, "*Spasibo . . . spasibo . . .*"

With an apparent effort, Landau twisted his mouth. "*Spa - si - bo,*" he whispered, barely audibly, laboriously breaking the word into syllables. But it was heard throughout Moscow: Landau had spoken.

"The first words he said were not spoken in his voice," Cora remembers. "It was as if they came from far away, from a stranger, a voice I didn't know and had never heard before. I remember thinking that it was the voice of a man who had returned from the dead."

A plastic tube still entered Landau's nose, leading to his stomach, for he could swallow only small amounts of water, but not food. Slowly, the swallowing reflex started returning and three days later, the catheter was removed from his nose. When Cora gave him his first spoonful of food, nurses and physicians stood by, for fear he might choke or swallow the wrong way. The opening in the trachea, though no longer needed for breathing, had not been stitched up but only covered with sterile cloth. If Landau choked, it could immediately be opened up to enable him to breathe, or to pump out any food that might have gone the wrong way.

"But nothing went wrong," remembers Cora. "It is amazing how slowly, how carefully he took his first bite, how long he chewed it, how long he hesitated to swallow it, realizing the danger and his weakness before it."

Then Landau started to remember.

Friends would mention incidents from his past, and

Landau would smile. His memory was vague at first. He could recognize a face he had known, but did not remember any name except Cora's. The early memories of his childhood and student days were the first to return. This, points out Professor Grashchenkov, was the expected pattern: in childhood and youth, the brain is less specific, less economical than in a grown man. It has not been trained yet, and it seems that a larger portion of the cortex takes part in the recording of the first memories. Later, regions of the brain become specialized for different types of thought process, and memories seem to become restricted to more specific areas.

Gradually, more recent memories returned, in an order generally following the chronology of his own life. He remembered Baku, Leningrad, Göttingen, and Copenhagen. He started recognizing his old friends. The first was Aleksei Abrikossov. A frequent visitor at the hospital, Aliosha stood by Landau's bedside one day, and Dau thoughtfully stared at him. "Do you recognize him?" asked a nurse. "Of course," answered Landau, hesitating a few seconds. "And who is he?" "A - lio - sha." "Is he a doctor, or a physicist?" "On fi-zik" [He is a physicist], said Landau slowly.

Neuropathologist Yelena Vinarskaya, psychiatrist Alexander Luriia, and other specialists sought to create special situations to stimulate speech, but the recovery of Landau's mind seemed to progress even faster than they had anticipated, as if the first word represented the breaking of a dam, followed by a sudden flood. Questions put to him in English, German, or French were understood as well as if they had been asked in Russian. Invariably, the answer came in the same language as the question, and frequently Dau repeated the same words. From the expression on his face, it was obvious that he enjoyed listening to his visitors.

On April 10, Doctor Fyodorov sat at Landau's bedside and started quoting some verses of Pushkin, one of Landau's favorite poets, whom nearly every Russian can quote at length. Fyodorov recited a verse from *Eugene Onegin:*

За что ж виновнее Татьяна?
За то ль, что в милой простоте
Она не ведает обмана
И верит избранной мечте?

Then, Fyodorov saw Dau smile and raise a hand. Fyodorov stopped, expecting a question, but Dau went on, slowly but unerringly . . .

За то ль, что любит без искусства,
Послушная влеченью чувства,
Что так доверчива она,
Что от небес одарена
Воображением мятежным,
Умом и волею живой,
И своенравной головой,
И сердцем пламенным и нежным?
Ужели не простите ей
Вы легкомыслия страстей?

Why is Tatiana, then, more guilty?
Is it because in sweet simplicity
Deceit she knows not and believes
In her elected dream?
Is it because she loves without art, being
Obedient to the bent of feeling?
Is it because she is so trustful
And is endowed by heaven
With a restless imagination,
Intelligence, and a live will,
And headstrongness,
And a flaming and tender heart?
Are you not going to forgive her
The thoughtlessness of passion?
            Eugene Onegin, trans.
            by Vladimir Nabokov,
            Bollingen Series LXII,
            New York: Pantheon Books.

Then Dau stopped and smiled proudly.

On April 14, Landau's niece, Maya Bessarab, wrote in her diary:

Now he changes from the Russian to the English language with surprising ease. He understands everything. When told that he was sick and that doctors were coming to visit him, he asked, "And how am I now?"

At the same time he mixes up many things. A nurse showed him a ring on her finger and asked, "What is this?" He replied, "A watch." When shown a portrait of Gagarin and asked who it was, his reply was, "Why, that's me!"

Motion had returned to the right side of the body, and now Landau started moving his left arm, then his left leg, in which there awakened an almost constant feeling of pain.

Toward the end of April, Landau was awarded for the second time the Lenin Prize for physics, his country's highest annual award for scientific achievement. Articles in the Soviet press mentioned the award, noting that Landau had suffered a severe automobile accident, from which he was now slowly recovering. Several feature articles were published about "The Miracle of Moscow," mentioning the unprecedented cooperation between scores of physicists and physicians, the visit of the foreign specialists, the hope for a rapid recovery.

A Western journalist was permitted to visit the bedridden scientist—Keith Morpett, the Moscow correspondent of the London *Daily Mail*. Dau prepared himself for the visit with excitement and talked to Morpett for several minutes, showing an unrealistic optimism that was the pattern during this stage of the recovery, an optimism that became a sort of crutch of hope to help him bear almost constant pain. Morpett quoted him as saying: "I shall be going home soon, and I shall rest there for a bit with my family. I think perhaps another week or so in the hospital here and I shall be ready to leave. I should like to get back to my work, of course, there is so much for me to do. But we shall see about that later. I am overwhelmed by the kindness so many people have shown me. I mean your countrymen too. I would like to thank them for all their help. I wish I could tell you I feel completely right again, and fit. But, I fear, that wouldn't be true."

On May 3, Maya Bessarab wrote:

He woke up in the morning and asked for his son, Igor. Igor arrived in the afternoon. They smiled quietly at each other, and then Dau started asking his son about his progress in school. There was one question which no one could understand except Igor because Dau spoke quietly and sometimes incoherently. The question was, "How are you getting on with the language?" He meant the English language, in which he had been tutoring his son.

Dau's friends tried to quiz him about physics. On May 6, postgraduate Anatoly Rusinov, the physicist on duty asked, "Dau, do you remember Pauli's paramagnetism?"

"Yes, I do."

"And do you remember Landau's diamagnetism?"

"Of course."

"How do these phenomena depend on temperature?"

"They almost do not depend on it at all."

"And what is the relation between them?"

"They are exactly proportional."

"What is the proportionality factor?"

"It amounts to about one third."

Maya's diary notes:

Dau remembers by heart his favorite maxims and quotations. He tries to write, but the handwriting is not very legible. "No one can be blamed for being born a slave," quoted Landau, and he wrote with his own hand the name of the author: Lenin.

May 10. His speech is much better today. "You don't look at all as though you wanted to sleep," a nurse told Dau. "No, but *you* certainly do," he answered. "Why don't you doze a bit, and if someone comes in I shall wake you up."

A physical and mental training program was established, but it had constantly to be changed. Generally, speech therapists and psychologists found that Dau seldom made an effort to take them seriously. He responded best when he became personally, emotionally involved, and the best therapy came from his friends who visited him and whose conversation interested him. He did become friendly with some of his physicians, but strongly resented others, and feared those whom he had associated with pain. "Psychiatrists," he said, "either try to bully you, or talk to you as if you were a child."

For instance, one of the Soviet Union's most renowned psychotherapists, Alexander Luriia, somehow antagonized Landau who stubbornly refused to cooperate with him. Luriia, who had treated countless soldiers whose brains had been injured during the war, had developed a deep understanding of such patients, and had devised methods that had been very successful in restoring brain function after injury. Luriia had found, for instance, that drawing certain geometrical figures helped patients organize and control their movements to overcome coordinating defects that were slow in being corrected during normal recovery. But when Luriia asked Landau to draw a circle, Landau drew a triangle. When he asked for a square, Dau penciled a star. When the perplexed therapist asked him to make a cross, and Landau wrote down a zero, Luriia shook his head in despair and scrutinized the physicist's dead-pan face, not knowing whether Landau was unable, or unwilling, to do what he was asked to do. Cora, who had seen her husband draw quite adequate geometric figures only a few days earlier, later asked him why he had done everything wrong.

"This man is ridiculous, and he asks me to do ridiculous things," said Dau. "I've been doing everything the other way round, just to get rid of him." Occasionally Dau even got angry; once a perplexed psychologist made a hasty retreat when the irate patient raised his voice and sharply criticized him as being incompetent in trying to treat him as if he were a child.

The restoration of mental functions progressed by spurts, in a complex, tortuous way. Sometimes Landau's mind could not reconstruct the most elementary notions, and sometimes his reactions were those of a healthy, exceptionally intelligent man who could tackle mathematical and logical problems a layman wouldn't understand at all.

His friends recognized traits of his character, and as a rule physicians were touched by his cordiality, politeness, and humor, and impressed by the unconventional frankness that had always been characteristic of his personality. Landau realized his condition, was conscious of his shortcomings, and embarrassed for imposing his helplessness upon so many of his friends. But he did not remember the accident, even refused to recognize that it happened, as if a strong mental block had been built around the event that brought him into the hands of death.

On May 16, Maya Bessarab noted:

Dau says, "I have become rather queer. . . . Naturally, one cannot ask for too much."

"What do you mean, too much?"

"Well, I mean I want my legs to start moving and my mind to remember everything, everything at once!"

May 18: "Damn it, I was certainly unfortunate. Do you think I shall ever be able to get out of this mess? Why is it that my legs hurt without being broken? I wonder whether medicine can really treat such a disease as mine."

May 20: "Things are pretty bad with me. Everything seems to be in a fog. What a funny thing has happened to me."

"You are very sick. You were in an automobile accident," [Maya told him].

"Somehow I don't believe very much that the accident ever happened."

On July 27, more than six months after the accident, Maya noted that Dau asked why he was not at home.

Conversations with physicians and psychologists now often seemed to bore him, and he was increasingly interested in "talking shop" with other physicists. For a time his colleagues provided him with the best mental therapy, remaining at hand to talk physics whenever Landau wanted to.

"How is his reasoning?" a doctor once asked Lifshitz, who had just spent some time at Landau's bedside.

"I think it's improving," answered Lifshitz, and proceeded to ask Landau to solve a complicated problem.

Thinking only for a short time, Landau gave his answer and closed his eyes to rest. The physician questioningly looked at Lifshitz, who sadly shook his head. "It's wrong," he whispered. Only later, as he mulled the problem over again, did Lifshitz realize that Landau's solution was correct. But Landau had developed the solution in such an unusual way that his approach hadn't even occurred to Lifshitz at the time.

On September 16, Maya wrote:

"What are you studying?" Dau asked a postgraduate student. "Ferromagnetism . . . and not everything is clear about it," came the answer. Dau immediately became quite animated. "Why do you say that? Everything seems to be clear enough," he said.

However, this awakening interest in physics that gave so much hope to Landau's friends seemed slowly to subside. Physicists realized that Landau became increasingly reluctant to talk shop. Perhaps he realized that the scientists who came to see him did not really come for a discussion nor to seek advice as they did when Dau's genius guided the Theoretical Physics Department at the institute. They came, instead, to help him, to find out how well he remembered, and how well he could reason. It was they who were testing him now, and perhaps he had become afraid of showing his weakness.

Professor Alexander Kitaigorodsky, who co-authored with Landau a book on *Physics for Everybody*, was talking to him once about his family problems (about which Landau was always ready to give his advice) when the conversation turned once more to physics. "Of course, I remember physics," said Landau, somewhat irritated. "And I can, right now in my head, solve a cubic equation. Can you?" But he realized that he did not remember everything. "I was so proud of my memory before," he sadly commented one day. "Now, I look into a mirror. I'm happy to see my own image in it. But it could just as well be some asinine mug, with long ears, instead."

Had Landau been any other patient, he might well

have been considered cured, said Grashchenkov. But he was not any patient. In his case, final recovery could not stop short of the exceptional faculties that had raised him to the ranks of the world's most renowned theoreticians. Any retraining program for an exceptional mind that had not functioned for so long obviously had to be empirical. It was not made any easier by the fact that Landau had always been something of a "character," whose patterns of thought seldom followed standard pathways. And the physicians and psychologists who were trying to help him recover were, again, treading on the thin ice of inadequate fundamental knowledge. Just what was it that they were trying to treat? What is the mechanism of memory, the anatomy of intelligence? How can these intangible faculties be related to the shape, the size, the particular manner in which billions of nervous cells may be assembled in the brain?

Since the discovery of electric potentials in the brain, it had been believed that electric currents, in some form of nervous impulses, permanently circulated through the brain to maintain memory traces, much as an electronic computer stores energy that has been fed into it. But more recent experiments have shown that the temporary interruption of these electric currents does not destroy memory, which must therefore, be imprinted in some other way. One of the now classical experiments showing this consisted of teaching hamsters to find their way through a maze, then chilling them into hibernation in a cold chamber below freezing temperature. This completely interrupted all electrical activity in the brain. But when the hamsters were thawed back from hibernation to active life, they still remembered their way about the labyrinth.

Likewise, it had been theorized that specific brain centers contained specific cerebral functions. This may be partly true, but it also seems that these functions can migrate from one area of the brain to another. For example, the left half of the brain (especially in right-handed people) usually not only controls the movements of the opposite side of the body but is the center of the higher human attributes. On the left side of the brain, the various centers are roughly distributed thus: the frontal lobe is the center of what is usually described as personality, relating to emotions, memory, and intellectual capacities. Behind it is the motor area, dispatching orders to muscles throughout the body, and underneath the motor area is the speech center. Farther back lies the sensory area, the center of the feelings of touch and of pain. (Both the motor and sensory areas, which stretch down from the top of the brain toward the temporal lobe, are subdivided into smaller areas corresponding to various parts of the body; these subdivisions run upside down: the upper area corresponds to the foot and the leg, the lower one to the face.)

Below the sensory area is the center of hearing, behind it a center for integration of sensory information and motor impulses, and in the occipital lobe at the back of the head the center for vision.

Memory in general, however, does not seem to be restricted to one area, but rather to be spread out through the entire brain. Varying parts of the brain of an animal, for instance, can be removed, yet the animal will continue to perform tasks it has learned. Amazingly enough, it does not seem to make any difference which part, or how much, of the brain is removed: as long as enough brain remains for the animal to survive, it remembers everything it has learned.

In man, the situation is infinitely more complex, as he

has a huge cortex which, unlike the animal's, continues to develop during childhood. Normally, the left part of the brain becomes dominant as the child begins to understand words, learns to use his hands, to talk, to write, and acquires a learned pattern of behavior quite unlike the animal's inborn instincts. But if an infant suffers severe damage to the left side of his brain, the right side develops, "learning" to do most things that the whole brain would normally do, and enabling the child to grow up with normal intelligence.

When a grown-up man is deprived of a portion of his cortex that has already become specialized to perform certain functions, another part of the brain can sometimes take over these functions, but not always. Such an adaptation is possible, for instance, in people who have suffered from a stroke that prevents blood from reaching certain parts of the brain. The affected regions become useless, but other areas can be trained to take over at least part of the disturbed functions. Some of the functions, however, may never be regained, or not as completely as they could be if the damage had occurred earlier, during childhood, when the brain was not specialized.

In the last decade there has been increasing evidence to indicate that memory is stored, not in the form of electric potentials, but chemically, as an accumulation of structural, biochemical alterations, spread through a large number of cells and in many regions of the brain. For many years there was no way of knowing just what type of structural change might be involved, and such a mechanism was first hypothetized simply because the electrical-storage theory was inadequate. One of the first hints to support the "biochemical theory" came from an apparently unrelated, somewhat weird research project undertaken by a young psychologist at the University of Michigan, James McConnell. With experiments on planarians— a type of pond-water flatworm about half an inch long —McConnell helped identify the chemical which appears to play the principal part in the storage of memory.

Planarians possess some anatomical peculiarities which McConnell was curious to explore: they are the lowest animals on earth to have a bilateral, symmetrical body, a central nervous system with a brain, and two symmetrical nerve cords with ladder-like cross-strands. They also, unlike earthworms, have a definite head and tail. Flatworms reproduce by "binary fission," becoming constricted halfway across the body and splitting in two. A few weeks after this effort, the tail half grows a new head, and the head half a new tail. (The head is easily identified by clearly visible, beady eyes, with an iris-like black spot that gives planarians a nasty, cross-eyed look. The eyes, however, do not form images but react only to the direction and intensity of light.)

McConnell first set out to determine whether the flatworms' primitive nervous system could enable them to "learn" anything at all. He built a simple conditioning device, consisting of a trough filled with pond water for the worms to move in, lights to flash upon them from above, and electrodes dipped into the water to give them a mild electrical jolt. The conditioning system was strictly Pavlovian: it consisted of flashing the lights, then jolting the animal with an electric shock. At first, flatworms ignore the light, but cringe at the electric shock. After one hundred or more successive jolts accompanied with a flashing of light, they "learn" to cringe at the light alone.

Later, McConnell and his colleagues at the University of Michigan wondered what would happen if a worm, conditioned to react to light, were to be sliced in two equal parts, the head on one side, the tail on the other. As expected, the tail grew a new head, and the head, a new tail. But less expected was the discovery that the new worm regrown from the tail remembered as much of the conditioning as did the one regrown from the head!

It seemed obvious that a chemical, spread throughout the worm's entire body (not only in its head) was involved in the storage of its primitive memory.

An even more uncanny experiment was yet to come. Conditioned worms (or, as they became affectionately known, "learned worms") were chopped up into small pieces, and dropped into a saucer containing untrained (or "naïve") flatworms. Planarians happen to be cannibalistic, and the "naïve" worms promptly ate bits and pieces of "learned" worms.

Amazingly enough, it appeared that the "naïve" flatworms acquired some of their victims' conditioned responses, by eating them. They had been, in the most literal sense of a term heretofore used in reference to electronic computers, "fed information." (Such a method, it was hinted by McConnell's students, could perhaps be usefully applied to high-level organisms, to help, for instance, naïve psychologists acquire information from learned ones.)

At any rate, there was no doubt now that a chemical was involved in planarian "memory," and further experiments by a number of biochemists permitted them to identify the chemical as ribonucleic acid (RNA), a substance occurring in the form of a long, double-stranded, helicoidal molecule, a molecule deeply involved in the reproduction, heredity, and growth processes of all living creatures.

In Sweden, Dr. Holgar Hyden, director of the Göteborg

Neurobiology Laboratory, showed independently that RNA also plays a part in the memory processes of higher forms of life. The RNA content in the brain of rats, for example, noticeably increases when the animals are trained to perform various tasks. Moreover, not only is the amount of RNA increased, but analysis showed that the molecules of RNA were also altered by learning. The nervous impulses coming to the brain, it seems, stimulated and transformed molecules of RNA, as if imprinting upon them a coded message which became memory.

This hypothetical process was confirmed again by studies with flatworms. If "learned" worms are sundered in two parts in the presence of RN-ase, an enzyme which destroys RNA or, in a more diluted form, prevents it from forming, the results are quite different from previous ones: the new worms grown from the head still remember their conditioning, but those grown from the tail do not. The enzyme did not destroy the RNA but only inhibited its formation. In the head, RNA—and memory—remained. But similar RNA in the tail half was prevented from duplicating itself and reaching the newly grown head, which remembered nothing.

Still later, the knowledge that RNA was involved in memory storage even found a clinical use. Senile patients receiving injections of RNA showed a marked improvement in their memory in comparison to those who received none. This usage of RNA, however, is severely limited because the injections may cause unpleasant side effects, particularly dangerous in patients whose physical condition is already poor or fragile.

Landau's physicians and the neurological specialists who treated him gathered many a time to review the most recent basic knowledge on memory and brain function, knowledge that was rapidly expanding even as Landau was recovering. They considered the possibility of RNA injections, a treatment which is still in the experimental stage, but rejected it as too hazardous. It seemed, anyway, that much of Dau's memory had returned without any other intervention than constant nursing, conservative rehabilitation, and frequent stimuli in the form of conversations with his colleagues and friends.

But even if a patient recovers much of his memory, he may not be fully capable of using this storage of information. Psychotherapist Alexander Luriia, who had treated thousands of wartime patients, wrote, in a monograph on "The restoration of function after brain injury," a description which could be applied to Landau some six months after his accident:

When such a patient is first seen, the impression may be that the wound has not caused appreciable disability and, apart from a slight clumsiness and slowness of his movements, the patient is otherwise perfectly normal. However, more careful investigation shows that patients of this group all have defects, possibly more serious than the disturbances of the specialized functions. These defects are associated with the breakdown of production activity and of active thought. The patient cannot utilize even those elements of his mental process which are most completely preserved. His complaint may be, "My thoughts will not flow . . . When I have to write a letter I don't know how to begin, and it takes me all day to write it." The patient usually replies readily to questions and shows no sign of disturbance of dialogue or reactive speech. He has considerable difficulty, however, if he is asked to give a detailed and lucid description of a picture or to write an essay on a particular topic. He then complains that he has nothing to tell, that he has difficulties in going beyond passive descriptions of what he sees, or reaching into the realm of active thought. . . .

In short, in this group of lesions the active flow of complex psychological processes is disturbed, though the basic inventory of thinking is preserved. The person becomes a being capable only of passive, reactive behavior, and deprived of the most precious assets of the human mind. We do not know the mechanism of actively flowing thought; we can only assume that it is connected with the creation of certain internal dynamic patterns for producing smoothly flowing "kinetic melodies" and with internal speech which is essential for fully developed thought.

Restoration may be possible, at least partial restoration of these internal dynamic patterns, says Professor Luriia. A patient will be able to tell a story with assistance, if provided brief stimuli in the form of questions, such as "What then?" or "what next?" Later, he can provide himself with such stimuli, and eventually train himself to do without them.

The description given by Professor Luriia closely fitted Landau: He had recovered much of his memory and of his ability to reason. He could answer questions intelligently and, provided the right stimulus, he could develop new ideas. But he usually engaged in such "active thinking" only in the presence of such a stimulus: a person he was particularly happy to see, an event that interested him, challenging questions asked by a physicist.

Further recovery, points out Luriia, is more difficult.

Sometimes, the patient can be taught to give himself the stimulus that he needs . . . The active process of restoration of function naturally demands a great deal of concentration and willpower, a diligent, steadfast work. The patient must have a clear awareness of his defect, and he must develop a need to compensate it. Intensive work, stability of motivation, are essential.

He must be encouraged by success—otherwise, he sees progress beyond his ability, and gives up. Then, he lowers the level of demands upon himself to prevent dissatisfaction in the future.

Quite frequently, Luriia notes, it is better for a patient not to resume the type of work he was engaged in before the injury, but to choose another job, in keeping with his natural turn of mind, but also with his capabilities.

Landau, after the rapid recovery of some of his faculties, had reached a stage at which he became discouraged: he had wanted to relearn "everything, right away," and failed. And he could not furnish the tremendous effort of willpower that would have been necessary to re-educate his mind, because he was constantly distracted by a strong, nagging pain in his left leg. Attempts to treat the pain with massages and heat or with other classical means, or even to relieve it temporarily with massive injections of Novocain, failed completely, indicating that the origin of the pain was not in the leg itself: neurologists believed the feeling of pain came from a cerebral lesion, probably in the sensory, pain-reception center for that part of the body. Progress in his recovery was practically arrested.

Landau could not imagine undertaking any other activity than research or teaching of physics, which had always been his *raison d'être*. Wilder Penfield, who returned to Moscow in October 1962 and visited Landau once more, remarked, "The type of mental process particular to theoretical physicists seems to be a rather peculiar one." And even though Penfield himself was in favor of a "second career" for that type of patient, he found it difficult to imagine what this new career could be in Landau's case. "Perhaps the patient could have taken up theology," he noted, only half-jestingly, "but in his country and in his case, this was rather unthinkable."

Physicians and psychiatrists were at a loss, unable once more to determine the future course of treatment, deeply frustrated because some of the basic elements of Landau's genius seemed to be intact, but the dynamism, the drive needed for further progress, was lacking.

"We could do no better than try to follow the classical line of mental rehabilitation training," says Professor Grashchenkov. "Memory had in great part returned, and the normal alpha rhythm of cerebral biocurrents was re-established throughout the entire brain. We just didn't dare do anything radical. We did think of trying the standard method of irradiating the portion of the brain where the pain originated, in the hope of destroying its focus, but we didn't dare. As long as there was a chance for Landau to recover his genius, we did not want to risk any damage that might make of him just a normal person."

CHAPTER 12

The Highest Reward—
and Hope

ON NOVEMBER 1, 1962, a telegram was delivered to the home of Lev Davidovich Landau. Cora had been taking care of his correspondence since the accident, passing on letters from prospective students to Lifshitz and Abrikossov, and taking Dau's personal mail to the hospital. He read all of it, but did not answer, insisting that he would get to it "in a few days," as soon as he felt better. Several hundred unanswered letters had accumulated in the nine months that had passed since the accident.

A few weeks earlier Landau had been transferred from the Burdenko Neurosurgical Institute to the exclusive Hospital of the Academy of Sciences off Leninski Prospect. An array of neurological personnel was no longer needed to treat him, and it was hoped that recovery would now follow its course with the help of rehabilitation specialists and psychotherapists. At the Hospital of the Academy, Dau had been given a sunny corner room with a small antechamber from which his nurses could keep an eye on him without disturbing him.

Usually Cora either walked or took a bus for the mile-long trip to the hospital but today, after opening the telegram, she ran out in the street and found a cab.

When she walked into Dau's room, he was complaining to a nurse about pain in his leg. The pain was as strong as ever, but now he felt it no longer in the region of his knee but lower down, in the ankle. It seemed as if pain had been slowly moving down his leg.

When his wife read him the telegram the pain immediately disappeared. Dau asked to see the telegram and read it over several times, whispering the words to himself as if to make sure they were right.

"The Royal Swedish Academy of Sciences today decided to award you the 1962 Nobel Prize for your pioneering theories concerning condensed matter, especially liquid helium."

Then Landau smiled, saying nothing.

The news rapidly spread through Moscow. On the radio, a musical program was interrupted to make the announcement of the award, which was followed by comments about Landau's achievements, his accident and slow recovery, about the glory of Soviet science, of the Communist Party, and of the Soviet people. The hospital buzzed with excitement. Most of the patients were scientists, either active or retired members of the Academy of Sciences, or members of academicians' families. Many walked over or sent messages to Dau's room to congratulate him, and a crowd of his friends quickly gathered, lining up in front of his room.

Many weeks earlier physicians had observed a pattern that had since become characteristic: whenever Landau became excited or interested, his pain disappeared, to return when his excitement subsided. Now, the pattern repeated itself. He forgot all about pain, smiled, and held forth with animation. His friends kissed him on both cheeks, beaming with pride as if they were sharing with him the honor that had been bestowed upon him. Now and then Dau corrected someone who mispronounced the title of the award and called it the "Nobiel Prize," with a "soft" b, the Russian way. "Not Nobiel—Nobel," said Landau, smiling. "Alfred Nobel was a Swede, not a Russian." And his students repeated, laughing, "Nobel."

The Nobel Prize is the most prestigious award that any scientist can hope for. In Landau's case, it came as a fitting conclusion to a long list of honors collected throughout his life. He was already a member of the Soviet Academy of Sciences, had received several state prizes, the Lenin Prize twice, the Max Planck medal, and the Fritz London prize. He was a member of the British Royal Society, of the Danish Royal Academy of Sciences, the Netherlands Royal Academy of Sciences; associate member of the National Academy of Sciences of the United States, honorary member of the American Academy of Arts and Sciences, of the Physical Society of London and of the French Physical Society.

"How sad," noted an editorial in the *Moscow Gazette of Literature*, "that the news of the Nobel award came to Landau in the hospital, and not at his desk, nor amidst the students' tumult in his lecture hall." There was not much hope that Landau would even be able to attend the traditional ceremonies in Stockholm on December 10, more than a month hence, when the Swedish people commemorate Alfred Nobel, when the laureates receive their gold medals from the hands of the King.

It was only when Landau became tired and his friends started to leave that he remembered he was bedridden, crippled. He remembered the pain in his ankle, which returned, nagging, persistent, and he wondered whether he would be well enough to travel, a month later, to Sweden.

For more than thirty years Landau had not been allowed to leave his country. Now, he knew, individual freedom in the Soviet Union, though still limited, was such as had not existed since the Revolution. There would be no official obstacle to his trip abroad, no endless paperwork, denials, and frustration.

What cruel irony that it was his own body now that might prevent him from traveling abroad, from taking a vacation after the ceremonies in Stockholm to visit some of the laboratories where he had spent the best months of his youth, to reminisce and laugh about the past with Rosenfeld, with Heisenberg, with Rudolph Peierls and with Peierls' wife, Genia, who studied with Landau in Leningrad such a long, long time ago. (How long? he wondered, counting with a smile: it had been nearly forty years.)

When Nikolai Grashchenkov sat by his bed later that day, Dau asked him to be frank. "Nikolai Ivanovich, please tell me truthfully: will I be up in a month?"

But physicians did not know. Landau's recovery had been almost completely arrested, yet, there was a new hope: the excitement of the award, Landau's strong desire to travel to Stockholm, might now fuel new energy and incentive. "It is in your own hands," said Grashchenkov. "If you work hard, if you make a great effort, perhaps you will be well enough to go. Otherwise . . ."

Physicians stepped up the rehabilitation program and

Landau amazed them with his stubborn courage. Did he need to walk? Day after day, in all weather, Dau dragged his nurses out to help him walk in the hospital garden. He refused to take the elevator from his room on the third floor, laboriously went down the steps and across the small wooden footbridge to the garden. Each step represented an effort that had to be calculated in advance. Wearing a warm *shuba*, a fur hat, a long scarf wrapped around his neck, Landau strained against the wind and the snow and the cold, and against pain. His feet were like stones, inert, stiffly held in orthopedic, ugly black boots laced to his ankles. For each step he threw one leg forward, shifted his weight, and gathered his energy for the next, walking like a puppet manipulated by an awkward puppetmaster. He tried to walk without his nurses' help, and they stood at one side while he leaned on canes braced to his forearms. If the nurses hadn't been nearby to support him when he faltered, he would have fallen to the frozen ground many times.

Every day he fought pain in the training room, hanging with his hands from a bar, trying to raise his legs. Pain subsided somewhat during the hot bath and the daily massage, but it seldom disappeared for long. He tried to read—novels, newspapers, scientific reviews—but he seldom could concentrate long before the pain again struck at his ankle, tearing his mind away. At night, sedatives were used to help him escape into painless, peaceful sleep.

November neared its end. Physicists realized there was no hope for Landau to recover sufficiently to make the trip to Stockholm, but he kept hoping. "Are you ready for the journey?" he asked Cora. "As for me, I think I shall be well enough next week."

In the first days of December, Sweden's ambassador to Moscow, Rolf Sohlman, was notified that Landau had not recovered, and would not be able to attend the ceremonies. Cora had a long talk with her husband, explaining that they would not go to Stockholm, but Dau still kept his optimism, believing that tomorrow perhaps, or the day after tomorrow, his pain would disappear. "But in any event, you must go, and take Igor with you," he told Cora. "It will be good for him to make the trip."

Cora's passport was ready and her reservations had been made for the flight to Stockholm, when she decided to stay at home. "I don't want to go," she said. "How can I leave, when Dau stays here, in bed, suffering? What will I do there, among the gay happy people in a banquet, when I will be sad and think about my Dau? I want to stay here, I want to be with my husband when he receives his medal, I want to help him if I can."

The Nobel Foundation, breaking its rule for the first time in time of peace, authorized the award and medal to be formally presented away from Stockholm, in Moscow, by the Swedish Ambassador. The ceremony was to take place in a conference room at the Hospital of the Academy of Sciences on December 10, the Nobel day in Stockholm, when the laureates would be receiving their awards from the King of Sweden.

The few people selected to attend the ceremony gathered in the conference room, while Landau prepared himself to come down. There was Mstislav Keldysh, the youthful, gray-haired mathematician and astronautical specialist, recently appointed President of the Soviet Academy of Sciences. There were Igor Tamm and Nikolai Semyenov, earlier Nobel laureates, and Piotr Kapitza, Landau's old friend, the director of the Institute for Physical Problems. Landau's arrival was announced, and they stood up.

It was a tense moment, as they waited for Dau to be wheeled into the conference room. Cora had helped him put on a fresh light-gray suit, and he sat in a wheelchair, asking if he looked all right. His nurses wheeled him down the hall and into the elevator and toward the door leading to the conference room, when Landau signaled them to stop. "I don't want to be wheeled in. I want to walk."

They helped him stand up. As he leaned on Cora's arm, she wanted to cry, but she didn't. A nurse opened the door and Landau walked in slowly, making an effort to remain erect, trying to smile. He took his seat at the head of a large conference table.

Rolf Sohlman, the veteran of the foreign diplomatic corps in Moscow, spoke fluent Russian, and it was in that language that he addressed himself to the physicist who listened attentively, smiling, his head slightly tilted to one side.

"In our country, in Sweden, the tenth of December marks the commemoration of Alfred Nobel. On that day all of the Swedish people honor the Nobel laureates and, in their person, the science and culture of the whole world," said the ambassador. "The Nobel foundation regrets, Mr. Landau, that you were not able to travel to Stockholm to receive from the hands of His Majesty, the King, the Nobel Prize in physics for 1962, but it hopes that you will have, later, the occasion to visit our country."

Ambassador Sohlman then quoted excerpts of the speech which was being pronounced in Stockholm by Professor I. Waller of the Swedish Academy of Sciences.

Briefly reviewing Landau's career, he went on: "Landau's ability to see the core of a problem and his unique intuition for physics appear clearly in his investigations on liquid helium. The natural helium gas had earlier been liquefied by cooling to about four degrees above the absolute zero of temperature and subsequent research had shown that this fluid, when further cooled to about two degrees, was transformed to a new state which has quite strange properties. According to a term introduced by Kapitza, it is superfluid, which means that it can easily flow through very fine capillaries and slits which almost completely prevent the flow of all other liquids. The originality in Landau's attack on the problem of explaining these phenomena was that he considered the quantized states of motion of the whole liquid instead of the states of single atoms as other scientists had done earlier. . . .

"The importance of Landau's investigation is apparent when one considers that an important goal of physical research is to explain the properties of liquids as completely as it has been possible to explain the properties of crystals or rarefied gases. In their efforts to attain this goal the scientists have in general met with unsurmountable difficulties. An essentail exception is Landau's theory of liquid helium which, therefore, is an achievement of great and profound importance.

"Besides his investigations on condensed matter, that is, matter in the solid and liquid state, for which he is now awarded the Nobel Prize, Landau has also made contributions of the utmost importance to other parts of physics, in particular to the theories of quantized fields and of elementary particles. He has, by his original ideas and masterly investigations, exercised a far-reaching influence on the evolution of the atomic science of our time."

When Ambassador Sohlman handed Landau the gold medal and the Nobel diploma, the Soviet scientist thoughtfully held them before him for a few seconds. His wife, wearing a nurse's white cap, stood behind him, her hands on his shoulders.

Then Landau spoke, softly but clearly, and if anyone in the room did not understand everything he said, it is not because it wasn't spoken distinctly, but because Dau had decided to speak in English. "I am deeply honored for this award," he said, asking the ambassador to convey his thanks to the Nobel Prize committee and his best wishes to His Majesty the King of Sweden. His friends remember that, in the true Landau fashion, he did not fail to introduce a note of humor into this solemn occasion. When Keldysh congratulated him, Landau returned the compliment. "Since we last met, I have heard that you have been named President of the Soviet Academy of Sciences. I congratulate you but, frankly speaking, I do not envy you."

Exactly a year after Lev Davidovich Landau received the Nobel medal from Ambassador Sohlman, the scientist was still at the Hospital of the Academy of Sciences, his condition practically unchanged.

True, his body now had completely healed, as completely as it ever would. Physical rehabilitation training had halved the difference in length between his legs, and the left leg was only about an inch shorter than the right. He could walk alone, leaning on two canes.

The "phantom pain," which he had first felt around his knee, then in his ankle, had gone down to the foot and finally to the little toe of his left foot. It was as strong and persistent as ever. It disappeared only when his mind became active or when he went to sleep—which he could now do without sedatives.

The pattern of his behavior had remained the same. When supplied with a stimulus in the form of something that interested him, Landau's mind became active. Otherwise, it was absorbed with pain. In the summer of 1963, for instance, when his son was preparing to enter Moscow University to major in physics, Dau became worried that Igor might fail the entrance examination. He asked for him and proceeded to give him a thorough test, making up problems which he jotted down on a sheet of paper, spending several hours questioning him. Late in the afternoon Dau was satisfied. "Don't worry, he'll make it," he told Cora—then the pain returned. A few weeks later Igor was accepted at the university.

When Professor Niels Bohr died in Copenhagen, on November 18, 1962, Dau was deeply disturbed but forgot his pain when he reminisced about his days in Copenhagen with the man he considered his master.

When President Kennedy was assassinated, Landau talked about it all day. Kennedy was liked and admired by many in the Soviet Union, and Landau compared his death with that of President Lincoln. He told his nurses the detailed story of the assassination a century earlier, and spoke at length about the possible repercussions of Kennedy's death on the world situation and on the problems of segregation in the Southern states. (Landau had always been angered by any form of racial discrimination, to such an extreme that he once even found it objectionable that a dermatologist pointed out in a scientific report the differences between the skin of whites and Negroes. "Why rehash differences that should be forgotten?" he commented.)

But aside from such moments of "reactive" interest, Landau was absorbed in pain, and kept putting things off "until tomorrow." He believed that tomorrow, perhaps, pain would vanish. Tomorrow, he might go home, and tomorrow, he would plunge into physics again. This constant hope that "the good things" would come in the near future seemed to give him a conditioned optimism, even with regard to events that had nothing to do with the state of his health.

Dau had long been a proponent, for instance, of drastic reforms in the Soviet system of education, particularly in the teaching of physics. "Children are taught false principles at first, only because these principles are easier to understand," he used to say. "Then, when they go on to higher education, they are told, in effect, that what they had learned was wrong, and are given new principles." Instead, Dau believed that physics should be started right off with the fundamental, though complex, truths, such as relativity and quantum mechanics, which can be presented in a simplified form. He would have manuals rewritten, the Soviet Pedagogic Academy eliminated, and new criteria established for the formation of teachers and professors.

Before his accident, however, he was rather pessimistic about the chances of such reforms against the "old guard," deeply rooted teaching methods. He had tried to write, in collaboration with Professor Alexander Kitaigorodsky, an elementary physics textbook which was never published as such; when it was printed in 1963, it had become a popular scientific book for the general public, called *Physics for Everybody*.

Now Landau became convinced that he could actually *do* something to carry out his projected reform. He talked

of writing to Nikita Khrushchev, whom he greatly admired for his "liberal policies" and for "rescuing the Soviet
Union from Stalin's ghost." Khrushchev, he said, might
help get things moving. Dau even conceded that he would
accept the post of Minister of Education, if it were offered
him.

Toward the end of 1963, he no longer particularly enjoyed visits from his friends, at least not long visits. He
seldom became interested in any project that represented
a concentrated mental effort. When the Pergamon Press in
England decided to publish a collection of his work, Dau
hardly took any interest in the selection of papers to be
included, but left the choice to Lifshitz. In earlier days,
Landau made it a point of honor not to publish anything,
particularly in foreign journals, that he did not find sufficiently significant.

Physicists and psychotherapists were completely at a
loss. "At first," remembers Grashchenkov, "we had wel-
comed pain as a good omen that meant feeling was returning to his body. But pain persisted, week after week,
month after month. We tried massages, heat treatment,
thermal baths, a barrage of Novocain injections—without
any success. There was no doubt that the pain resulted
from damage to the brain, probably affecting a small region, perhaps only a few cells, in the thalamus, the mass
of gray nerve matter at the base of the brain."

But the neurologists could not—or dared not—do anything, for fear of inflicting further damage to the brain. A
standard method of treatment, explains Grashchenkov,
would have been to irradiate the appropriate area with X
rays. But this is a "shotgun treatment," which works by
destroying a few more cells in the affected area to sup-
press the pain impulses. The destruction of these cells
might possibly prevent complete mental recovery later.

"We didn't know any longer what we could do to help," says physicist Abrikossov, who had spent many days and nights at Landau's bedside. "Dau didn't want to talk, didn't want to read, to make any effort. As soon as we tried to engage him in a conversation, he complained of his leg again." Lifshitz, together with some of Landau's physicians, wondered whether the pain he was complaining about had not become a sort of defense mechanism, brought up whenever he wanted to avoid an effort. "We started wondering," says Lifshitz, "whether Landau would ever come back to work with us again."

Toward the end of December, physicians decided that Landau should return home, even if pain persisted. In addition to his pain, Dau was now sinking deeper into a condition known as the "hospital syndrome," a general apathy, an indifference that threatens to overcome any patient who remains bedridden for many months: the hospital becomes a sort of a cradle, isolating and protecting the patient from the reality of the outside world.

Masons and plumbers went to work in the small apartment facing the Institute of Physical Problems. A double banister was built along the staircase leading to the second floor. A door was pierced from Landau's room, leading into a room that normally belonged to the apartment next door, where a bathroom was installed.

Everything else was preserved as Landau had left it almost two years earlier when he started on his drive to Dubna: his desk facing the window and the institute, a cartoon showing himself in the guise of Don Quixote in armor, followed by Lifshitz as Sancho Panza, storming a windmill in which the captive was—a blonde waitress; a bookcase bulging with reviews and textbooks, and a shelf reserved for Landau's many awards, which now contained the Nobel scroll. A long, narrow bed, above which there hung the photograph of a pretty young blonde girl, who represented his ideal of beauty.

I had already made two trips to Moscow after Landau's accident, and had finally obtained some sort of official sanction to write a story about "the Miracle of Moscow." Landau's wife, some of his friends, physicians, and a few physicists at the Institute of Physical Problems had willingly contributed some of their impressions and reminiscences, but in spite of persistent pleas on my part, no one would take the responsibility of bringing a foreigner to visit Landau himself.

In desperation, I took a cab to the Hospital of the Academy of Sciences the day before my scheduled departure from Moscow shortly before Christmas of 1963, a few days before Landau was to return home. A nurse at the door instructed me to take a white hospital gown, the required garb for any visitor, which was given in exchange for one's overcoat. As I walked toward the elevators, *Pravda* in hand, the admission clerk stopped me. "Where are you going, *tovarishch?*" she asked. "To have a chat with Landau," I answered, in my best Russian, with all the nonchalance I could muster. "Wait a minute," she said, picking up the telephone and dialing a number. It seemed to be busy and she hung up, shrugging. "Do you know where he is?" "Yes," I lied. "Go right ahead."

I plunged into the first elevator and pressed a button. I stepped out into a clean, whitewashed hall, walked purposefully to an aging nurse and asked her to show me Landau's room. "You're on the wrong floor," she said, and showed me the way.

Two nurses sat in a small antechamber. "May I see Lev Davidovich?" I asked. "How is he?"

"Not too well. But come in, please." We walked into a sunny room. To the left, against the wall, on a narrow hospital bed, a thin figure lay curled up, facing the wall. Only a mane of graying hair showed from under the blanket. A nurse placed her hand on his shoulder: "You have a visitor, Lev Davidovich."

Slowly, Landau turned around. In his left hand, he held a nipple-topped bottle of water to drink from. Gently, his nurses helped him sit up.

I introduced myself and we shook hands. He spoke perfect English, but in the soft, sometimes hesitant voice of a man who has long been bedridden. I told him I hoped to write his story.

"Do you find enough to say?" he asked, and then answered a few questions. "Of course I hope to go back to physics, but I cannot yet, not as long as I have pain. I never could tolerate pain. The slightest pain could stop me from working.

"I remember physics. But you know, it has been two years now. In two years, much new happens in physics these days, and I will have much to catch up with.

"I think my memory has recovered, but it goes only far back, before I became ill. Now, I do not remember every detail from day to day, and perhaps this is good. If I remembered, I would only have the memory of pain. Pain is with me every day, and it is better not to have the memory of constant pain.

"But I have much hope. Now the pain goes down to my foot, and only the toe is hurting. Perhaps it will go away completely, and this can happen any time. Perhaps today, perhaps tonight. I keep hoping but, of course, I cannot know. Perhaps it will take a week, or a few weeks. Now the pain bothers me so much that I cannot concentrate even to read, not even a newspaper."

When I told Landau about some of his old friends abroad, he smiled. The eyes were clear; the eyelid over the left eye still drooped slightly, and a scar was visible on his forehead. But that pain was forgotten. He asked questions, wanted to make sure that I was comfortably seated. "I hope your work is not too difficult. I would like to help you, but now, I cannot. Please thank everyone who was so wonderful to me, people everywhere, whom I don't even know. And come to see me when I am better. I should be going home soon, and I should be better there."

So much suffering was written on his face that, strangely enough, one could almost feel guilty. Awkwardly, he autographed *Physics for Everybody*. As I took leave, his handshake was weak. "Come back again, if you have time," he said.

His nurses were happy that Dau had been distracted from pain for a while, but as I walked out, he turned against the wall again, suffering. The nurses asked me when I was leaving, insisted that I should visit Landau again. "It does him much good, to talk like that. Please come back if you have time," they said, smiling, and added, "But you want to be home for the holidays. So, happy new year!"

Without undue optimism, I applied for a two-day extension of my visa, and it was promptly granted. Now I returned to the hospital with the assurance of a regular visitor. I talked to Landau in his room once more, walked with him in the hospital garden on the day before he returned home.

There was a biting *mitiel*, the same type of light snow flurry that swept through Moscow in the morning of

January 7, 1962, almost two years earlier, when Sudakov
was driving Landau along Dimitrovsky Highway.

"You see," said Dau, straining against the wind-blown
flakes, leaning against the canes braced on his forearms.
"You see, I am far from well yet. My foot hurts, and I
must go in to rest now. If you have time, please come
back tomorrow. Tomorrow, I may be better."

In January, 1964, Professor Lev Landau left the Hospital of the Academy of Sciences to return home.

The apartment in which he had lived so long, and from which he had walked out one cold morning two years earlier, seemed strange to him. The staircase leading to the second floor had been widened, a new bathroom built next to his room, and steel handles had been attached to the walls, the banister, and even to his bed, to enable the scientist to grasp one handle, then another, as he walked along, haltingly, but without crutches.

In a letter describing the scientist's condition, Professor Grashchenkov wrote later that throughout 1964 Landau had the same trouble with pain in his left foot. Twice, Dau received "very massive" injections of procaine and novocain in the leg. A few minutes after the first anesthetic was injected, the pain disappeared completely. Landau walked about with ease and, on the following day, took up with enthusiasm the reading of physics journals that had been set aside for him. But in the afternoon, less than 24 hours after the injection, pain returned, as severe as it had been before. Discouraged, Landau gave up his efforts. A second injection was given, but the pain this time did not disappear completely before returning as strong as ever.

"Since the beginning of the summer," wrote Grashchenkov, "Landau lived in his country house near Moscow, a very charming place. He improved his movements, used virtually no supports, and walked long distances without help. Sometimes his pain disappeared for four or five hours without any medicine."

During that summer, Landau wrote a long article which appeared on July 8, 1964, in the *Komsomolskaya Pravda*, on the occasion of the seventieth birthday of his friend, Piotr Kapitza. Much of the article was devoted to Kapitza's achievments as a scientist, to his kindness and honesty. Landau also revealed for the first time in the Soviet press that he himself had been imprisoned in 1938 as a spy:

"In 1938 Kapitza discovered what were then astonishing events, occurring in liquid helium—and I explained these events theoretically," wrote Landau. "We met frequently at that time, and talked at length. From Kapitza, I learned much that I could not have learned from anybody else. . . . I also have, of those years, a very sad memory. Following a wanton denunciation, I was arrested. I was accused of being a German spy. Today, this sometimes seems amusing to me but then, believe me, it was no laughing matter. I spent a year in jail, and it was clear that I couldn't have survived even another six months. I was simply dying. Kapitza drove to the Kremlin and demanded my freedom; otherwise, he said, he would have to leave the Institute. I was freed. Need I say that such an action, in those years, required no little courage, great humanity, and a crystal-clear conscience."

During the summer, Landau also coached his son, Igor, who studied physics at Moscow University. During brief respites from pain he read newspapers and professional journals, but the respites were never long enough, says Grashchenkov. "Landau has improved physically and psychically, but he is still not very active in his special work," he wrote. "I am unable to tell you anything about his future recovery. In any case, I strongly believe that he will recover slowly but surely. Time is the best doctor."

But pain persisted, and physicians wondered again whether it did not result from the pinching of a nerve in the hip. They considered severing the root of the nerve leading to the toe, and at the end of December, 1964, Landau returned to the Hospital of the Academy of Sciences. But in January, 1965, he returned home—without an operation: "The pain," said Cora, "seemed to recede again, and now it seems it comes only from a tiny tip of the toe. So, the operation was given up. Dau is tired of pain and he doesn't work much aside from helping Igor—who has just successfully passed his exams. But we feel now that the ordeal is slowly coming to an end."